VIADUCTS AND

Swan With Two Necks.

R. a. Isquall '96

A CELEBRATION OF REAL ALE IN STOCKPORT'S PUBS

RESEARCHED BY MEMBERS OF THE CAMPAIGN FOR REAL ALE

EDITED BY ALASTAIR L. WALKER

CONTENTS - AREAS

CONTENTS - ARTICLES

Viaducts and Vaults 3, A Celebration of Real Ale in Stockport's Pubs. First Published 2003.
Published by CAMRA, The Campaign for Real Ale Ltd, 230 Hatfield Road, St Albans, Herts AL1 4LW
Tel: 01727 867201 on behalf of Stockport & South Manchester Branch of CAMRA
© CAMRA Ltd. 2003

ISBN 1-85249-188-4

Printed by Redvers Press, 615 Oldham Road, Failsworth, Manchester M35 9AN
Typesetting by CPPR, 8 The Green, Heaton Norris, Stockport, Cheshire SK4 2NP (Phone & Fax 0161 432 8384) using CPPR Autopage database publishing software. This publication was set using Adobe Pagemaker 7.01, Adobe Illustrator, Adobe Photoshop, Corel Draw and Altsys Fontographer, Typefaces used in this publication are Humanist 521, Humanist 531 & Frutiger (Humanist 777) for the listings, Benguit Medium, Palatino, Pal85C, and Goudy Sans MT.

VIADUCTS AND VAULTS 3

WELCOME to the third edition of Viaducts and Vaults, a guide to, and celebration of, the real ale pubs of Stockport Metropolitan Borough. The first two editions of this guide both won prestigious publication awards from the Campaign for Real Ale (CAMRA) nationally, so there is a hard act to follow.

All articles and pub descriptions are completely new and all survey information has been totally re-checked by a dedicated band of unpaid local CAMRA volunteers. The guide consists of a comprehensive listing of all pubs in the borough and the editorial content and pub selections are completely independent of any breweries, pubs or other organisations. No money has been offered, received nor requested from any pubs selected and advertising from individual pubs was prohibited. The pub entries fall into three general categories, democratically decided upon by the members of the Stockport and South Manchester Branch and the High Peak and North East Cheshire Branch of CAMRA. The most highly recommended real ale pubs have comprehensive information on facilities, an extensive description and an accompanying photograph or illustration. The remaining real ale pub entries contain basic critical information as well as a brief description. As a public service, we have also listed all of the current keg-only venues so that the reader knows which ones to avoid, if he/she is a devotee of cask beer. Unfortunately, since the last edition of this guide, the percentage of local keg-only outlets has risen alarmingly in reflection of the situation nationally, in which cafe bars and themed outlets have infested the country with tasteless, megabrand Euro-fizz.

As for all publications everywhere, we cannot guarantee the complete accuracy of all of the information in this guide, nor can we accommodate changes that have occurred after the manuscript has gone to the printers.

CHEERS AND HAPPY DRINKING   ALASTAIR L. WALKER, EDITOR.

ACKNOWLEDGEMENTS

THE production of a guide like this is a bit like having a baby - you don't realise how much time, effort and stress-management it takes until you have actually gone through the experience yourself! The whole process would be impossible without the commitment of a dedicated group of local CAMRA stalwarts who have given their time and energy completely free and with considerable enthusiasm.
In particular, my thanks go to the following:

Karen Wainwright - *sub-editor*

Paul Hutchings - *design and layout, database manager*

Chris Wainwright - *photographs*

Mark McConachie - *map coordination, public transport information, directions, last minute goal line clearances*

Jim Flynn - *advertising, publicity, sponsorship*

Paul 'Freddy' Formby - *organisation, progress chasing, general encouragement.*
All article writers are acknowledged at source.

Last, but not least, my heartfelt thanks go to all of the unpaid surveyors who braved the wilds and weather of Greater Stockport to seek out the relevant knowledge (and beer!)
ALASTAIR L. WALKER, EDITOR

Lots of things can drive you to drink...

...but public transport will drive you back

GMPTE

Better travel by bus, train and tram

GREAT PUBS, GREAT PINTS, AND ALL ON YOUR DOORSTEP.

WELL, not *quite* on your doorstep. It's unlikely there are half a dozen great pubs that you've never tried before within walking distance. If this guide has whetted your appetite to venture beyond your local then you need to consider the best way to get there. Obviously you won't want to take the car; so what are the alternatives? Buses trains and trams of course.

If you don't know your 192's from your 378's or if the last time you caught a train there was a steam engine at the front then you need help. That's where GMPTE come in. They're responsible for providing information about ALL the public transport in Stockport and throughout Greater Manchester.

So if you want help planning your journey than ring the GMPTE enquiry service 0161-228 7811 and they will advise the best way to get there. If you've got internet access then visit www.gmpte.com - where there is an electronic journey planner.

You'll need a ticket for every journey – either buy it on the bus or from the ticket office (or on the train if closed). If you're planning a day out then ask about the Daysaver ticket range that lets you make as many journeys as you wish. To get you started each of the listings in this guide show a brief summary of the public transport passing nearby.

One last word of advice – most public transport runs until around last orders – but don't forget to check the time of the last one home!

Better travel by bus, train and tram

GMPTE

PUBLIC TRANSPORT IN STOCKPORT

ALTHOUGH Stockport is well served by trains from Manchester, with reasonable service levels to places such as Hazel Grove, Bramhall and Cheadle Hulme, the local rail network is not a great deal of use for travelling to places local to Stockport. For that reason, most of the public transport information provided here is bus-related.

Where to get information

❂ Stockport Bus Station has a GMPTE Travelshop which is open 0700 - 1730 Mon - Sat. They can provide timetables, travel maps, weekly / monthly tickets, journey planning and much more.

❂ Stockport Bus Station is located by the River Mersey, to the west of the A6 Wellington Road and Mersey Square Shopping Centre

❂ If you cannot get to the Travelshop, you can get bus times on the phone from the GMPTE Enquiry Line 0161-228 7811, daily from 0800 to 2000. You can also use the national bus enquiry line, Travelline on 0870 608 2 608. The GMPTE website www.gmpte.com also gives timetable information and a very useful electronic journey planner.

Getting started *(Points to note)*

❂ All bus services listed in this guide as serving a pub are 'core services', that is, they run evenings and, usually, all day Sunday too. During the day, other services may serve that pub, but are omitted on the grounds of clarity

❂ All services begin from Stockport Bus Station, unless otherwise stated in the text

❂ Other than the Bus Station, the main boarding points are the A6 Wellington Road opposite Grand Central, St. Petersgate, Warren Street and Greek Street

❂ Stagecoach Manchester provides the majority of the services in Stockport Borough. However, evening and Sunday journeys are often run by a different operator, so it is well worthwhile checking this before considering purchasing a single-operator return, or multi-ride ticket

❂ Where a Rail station is shown in the pub listing, this indicates that the station is a half-mile or less away from the pub. The station name is only given where it differs from the area name

Tickets *(all prices correct at time of going to press - May 2003)*

The GMPTE Daysaver ticket range offers good value for days out and evening trips where you are visiting a number of places. A number of weekly and monthly travel tickets are available from GMPTE and individual operators - check with GMPTE for details. Listed below are the daily tickets available to you.

❂ Single fare - the simplest option. Just pay for each journey as needed

❂ System One Day Saver - buy it from the driver of the first bus you board that day; it is valid all day, for an unlimited number of journeys, on any operator's bus throughout the whole of Greater Manchester. Cost is £3.30

❂ System One Bus & Rail Saver - buy it on the first bus or train you board that day; it is valid all day after 0930hrs, for an unlimited number of journeys, on any operator's bus or any rail service throughout the whole of Greater Manchester. Cost is £3.80

❂ Stagecoach Day Rider - validity is much like the System One ticket. However, it is ONLY valid on Stagecoach Manchester and Magicbus services. Thus, you may end up forking-out for additional fares if the bus you need is operated by another company. Cost is £2.60

❂ Rail Ranger - unlimited travel in Greater Manchester on any rail service. Valid 0930hrs onward (all day at weekends). Cost £2.50

❂ Evening Rail Ranger - unlimited travel in Greater Manchester on any rail service. Valid 1830hrs onward. Cost £1.25

MILD IN STOCKPORT BY MARK MCCONACHIE

NOT too many years ago, it was a widely held opinion that only three strong-holds of mild drinking were left in the UK - the West Midlands, South Wales, and right here, in the North West. Sadly, I am no longer convinced that is true, for even these heartlands of mild consumption have been battered in recent times by the on-slaught of lager and the so-called 'smooth' beers. Locally, this unwelcome blight has manifested itself to such an extent that in nearby towns such as Bolton, Wigan and Rochdale, cask mild is indeed a rare beast. Happily, the same is not true of the mild scene here in Stockport.

What is mild anyway, I hear some of our younger readers ask? Mild ale (to give it its proper name) is merely a lightly hopped beer that is also often, but not always, sweeter than your friendly neighbour-hood session bitter. In addition, its strength is usu-ally lower than that of typical bitters (though there are some notable exceptions!). Of course, a lower strength, tasty beer means you can enjoy more of it at a single sitting without succumbing to the effects of its higher gravity stable mates. As to the colour of the beer, milds range from the light and mid-browns, right through to a deep brown/black.

So now that you know all that, I suppose you are eager to go out and try some of these delicious beers. Well, with this guide in your hand, you are never very far from a pub offering top quality cask mild. Our very own home town brewer, Robinson's, leads the pack by sheer weight of numbers - they have more pubs in the borough than anyone else and as most of those sell mild, it is a fair bet you will come across a pint if you visit a Robinson's house. Their most widely available mild is called simply Hatters (an allusion to the town's once famous hatting industry). Previously called Best Mild, it received a marketing makeover some years ago to broaden its appeal. This, together with production im-provements, have seen its popularity maintained. Hat-ters is a mid-brown beer that also has a much rarer, almost black sibling Hatters Dark. Although ostensi-bly just Hatters with added caramel, this version has a distinctly richer and sweeter taste that some customers prefer and is definitely worth seeking out.

Moss Side brewer, Hydes, produce three milds - Mild, Dark Mild and Light. The first two have similarities in colour to the relative Hatters beers, whereas the Light is much paler in colour with a slightly higher gravity. Without exception, all of their pubs in this guide will offer one, if not two, of these beers.

Joseph Holt, of North Manchester, may only have four pubs in the town, but this brewer's reputation for strong and uncompromising beers means it is al-ways 'punches above its weight' in the minds of lo-cal drinkers. Although the popularity of their bitter is undisputed, sales of mild have dropped consider-ably and in some pubs this beer has unfortunately

been replaced with 'smooth' mild. Almost black, and very bitter for a mild, this beer is luscious and very more-ish when found on good form.

Until recently (Dec. 2002), J.W. Lees of Middleton, sold their unusual GB Mild in their sole tied house in the area, the Travellers Call at Bredbury. Poor sales saw the end of it, however, so you will have to ven-ture closer to their heartland to sample this brown, slightly sweet, but characterful beer.

Cains of Liverpool, made an impact on the area when they acquired the Gothic Bar in Gatley. So too did their tasty, roasted, dark mild which often turns up as a guest in ex-Greenalls houses.

Local microbrewers have also managed to make their presence felt in no small way in the town. First on the scene was the Porter Brewing Co., with their ex-tremely dark and dry Dark Mild (always available at the Railway, Portwood). Most recently, at the Navigation, Heaton Norris, two mild beers from Beartown can be found adorning the bar - Ambeardextrous, a fairly light brew, and the dark and dangerous Black Bear at a hefty five percent ABV. Of the national brewers products, not a lot of mild is to be found in the area (or in the rest of the known universe for that matter). You may happen across such as Tetley mild (and Tetley Dark), Greene King XX mild, Banks's Original and perhaps even Webster's Green Label but don't count on it.

To gain a better appreciation of mild ales, and the pubs in which they are sold, your best bet is to try a local brew-er's outlet or one of the multi-beer free houses, such as Ye Olde Vic, Crown (Heaton Lane) and the Railway in Portwood. Late May of every year sees Stockport Town Hall as the venue for the Stockport Beer & Cider Festi-val, at which prestigious event there are always a good selection of milds of differing styles and strengths to be had. Two months prior to the beer festival, the local branch of CAMRA hosts the 'Stockport and Manchester Mild Challenge' - a passport scheme whereby drinking mild in enough of the participating pubs can reward you with free entry and free pints of mild at the beer festival, commemorative T-shirts and much more, in a campaign-ing and enjoyable celebration of this most British of beer styles. Happy (mild) drinking.

STOCKPORT AND ENVIRONS BY ALASTAIR L. WALKER

NOT so much gleaming spires and cavalcades as steaming chimneys and shopping arcades but this tongue in cheek description would do modern-day Stockport a disservice as the town currently has an air of confidence, optimism and vibrancy.

Unfortunately, this is not quite true of the town's football league team which, at the time of writing, is facing a second successive relegation to a lower division. Come on you County! The club's nickname is 'the Hatters', reflecting one of Stockport's major local industries in previous times. In fact, it is only very recently that Christy's hat makers closed their doors for the last time and ended a century long supply of top hats to the world's toffs. The award-winning Hat Museum adjacent to the main bus terminus tells the story of the industry and is a good bet for a mid-afternoon break. The modern shopping centre has the usual preponderance of multi-national famous names and 'big shed' retail zones and although most of the oft-quoted 'dark satanic mills' have now been obliterated, a few enclaves of old Stockport have managed to survive. Foremost of these is the old market place and surrounding streets and alleyways, including Underbank, Chestergate, the Hillgates, St.Petersgate and Millbank. The splendid Victorian Market Hall was almost demolished

but public outcry led to it being fully restored to its original condition and it now provides a fitting centre-piece to the colourful outdoor market that prospers on Fridays and Saturdays and meanders past the Parish Church and Staircase House. The latter is in a row of some of the oldest buildings in Stockport and contains an intact Tudor staircase but sadly is not currently open to the public due to its dangerous state resulting from a recent roof collapse. Not surprisingly, some of the town's architecturally more interesting pubs are found in this area and several of these still have cellar links to the extensive subterranean tunnel network that exists underneath the town. Originally constructed centuries ago when the long since demolished Stockport Castle held a prominent position atop the Market Place mound facing the approach to Lancashire across the River Mersey, the tunnels were still in use during the second world war as air raid shelters and are rumoured to extend as far as Lyme Hall near Disley. The tunnels can be visited by heading away from Mersey Square along

the right hand side of the old Co-op building for 100 yards until reaching the entrance foyer on the right. For devotees of ancient historic country houses, the aforementioned Lyme Hall and its grounds lie just outside the area covered by this guide and are open to the public, as is the less grandiose but equally interesting Bramall Hall which is situated just inside the southern boundary of the borough. For the more adventurous, a slightly longer journey to Tatton Hall or Dunham Massey will provide a full day's diversion for those intending to stay a bit longer in the area. If looking for a shorter distraction whilst in the Marple area, then a visit to the famous stepped locks at the canal is a must, or a stroll in the Etherow Nature reserve at nearby Compstall should help to drum up a thirst in the afternoon. Back in town, the museum and grounds of Vernon Park are worth a visit and the northern part of the Peak District National Park is only a short trip away from the centre of Stockport by public transport. Add a liberal sprinkling of some of the finest beers and best town pubs in the country and you can see why we are proud to recommend a visit to Stockport and its surrounds.

CHEERS.

HOW TO USE THIS GUIDE

The areas of Stockport are listed alphabetically, except where adjacent areas share complex boundaries where they have been grouped together. Hence pubs in Cale Green, Edgeley and Heaviley can be found listed together, as can those in Compstall and Marple Bridge; Gatley and Heald Green; Heaton Chapel, Heaton Moor and Heaton Norris (called the Heatons for convenience). All areas which contain featured pubs have an accompanying Map (details of which can be found on page 10) and have a map reference for ease of identification. Each featured pub has a full listing like the one below, and a photograph. Other entries are similar in form, but contain fewer details and have shorter descriptions. An index listing all the pubs in Stockport can be found on page 86

PUB NAME AND MAP REFERENCE ☞ **WAGGONLOAD OF MONKEYS   Z4**

ADDRESS AND TELEPHONE NUMBER ☞ 1349 The Long and Winding Road, SK0 3XX
Tel: 0161 666 0001

DIRECTIONS & PUBLIC TRANSPORT ☞ *junction of General Ludd Road*
BR (Cemetery), Buses: 097, (383 no return)

HOURS OF OPENING & ☞ **5 - 11 Mon - Fri, 12 - 5 Sat, 12 - 10.30 Sun**
FOOD SERVICE ☞ *Main Meals: 12 - 2.30 & 5 - 7 Mon - Fri, 12 - 6 Sat*

DRAUGHT BEER & DISPENSE METHOD ☞ **Bells Enoch Bitter   H**
Clarke's Excalibur Extra-Strong Mild   H
Waterloo Boney's Ruin   G

DESCRIPTION ☞ A rare outlet in Stockport for beers from extinct local breweries, this pub was, for many years, under threat of demolition from a proposed new canal. However, now the future looks much more secure with the addition of a railway siding next to the pub stables for direct delivery of beers. A fine local that has suffered somewhat from over-enthusiastic refurbishment by a neo-Georgian architect. It is rumoured town-gas lights are to be fitted. Over the last few years travellers coming from the direction of Stockport have frequently been the victims of local highway robbers. Nowadays the locals are of a friendlier disposition and a warm welcome is assured.

BEER DISPENSE	
H	Handpump
E	Electric pump
G	Gravity

FACILITIES (SEE BELOW FOR KEY) ☞   🚐 ❀ ✄ 🍃

🚐	Large Carpark	❀	Other outdoor drinking area	🁣	Dominoes
🚗	Small Carpark	🪑	Pub has Children's Certificate	🧍	Other pub games
✄	No Smoking area	🎋	Inside play area / family room	♿	Disabled Facilities
🔥	Real Pub Fire (not gas)	🎏	Children's area outside	▮	Pub uses lined 'oversize' glasses
Q	Quiet Pub (no piped music)	🍺	Vault (separate public bar)		
❀	Beer Garden	🎯	Darts		

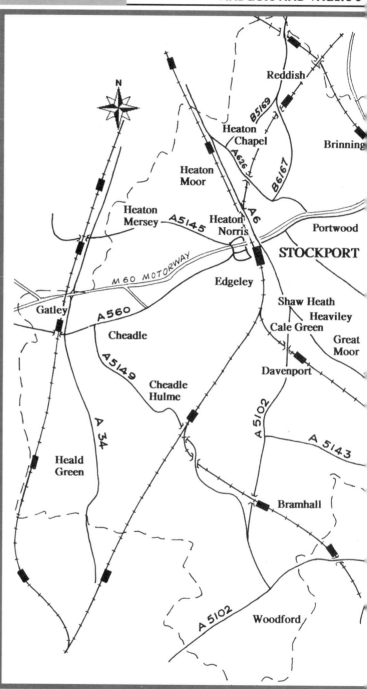

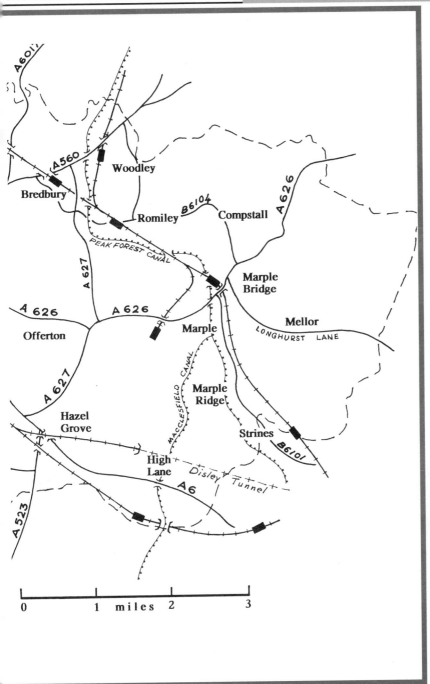

A
R
E
A

C
O
V
E
R
E
D

B
Y

T
H
I
S

G
U
I
D
E

BRAMHALL

BELUGA CAFE BAR
26 Bramhall Lane South, SK7 1AF
NO REAL ALE

BRAMHALLS
9 Bramhall Lane South, SK7 1AL
NO REAL ALE

BROMALE
West Park Road, SK7 3JX
off North Park Road/Bramhall Park Road
12 - 11 Mon - Sat, 12 - 10.30 Sun
Guest Beer   H
An imposing pub tucked away in a residential area. Wood-panelled throughout, the entrance lobby affords access to a large lounge and lively vault, which is mainly occupied by the regulars and often has sport showing on the big screen.

LADYBROOK HOTEL
Fir Road, SK7 2NP
junction of Waterloo Road
12 - 11 Mon - Sat, 12 - 10.30 Sun
Boddingtons Bitter   H
Three Guest Beers   H
Large, imposing 1930s building with comfortable interior. Guest beer from Scottish & Newcastle's list. Dining is available throughout but does not dominate excessively.

ORANGE TREE
Ack Lane East, SK7 2BY
junction of Bramhall Lane South
11 - 11 Mon - Sat, 12 - 10.30 Sun
Boddingtons Bitter   H
Two Guest Beers   H
An upmarket cafe-bar. Airy and light interior. The emphasis is on dining without being detrimental to drinkers.

SHADY OAK
Redford Drive, SK7 3PG
off Grange Road/Ringmere Road
4 - 11 Mon - Fri, 1 - 11 Sat, 1 - 10.30 Sun
Tetley Bitter   H
Morland Old Speckled Hen   H
Guest Beer (Occasional)   H
Comfortable estate pub in the open-plan style but with a number of distinct drinking areas around the central bar.

SHIRES BAR
County Hotel, Bramhall Lane South, SK7 2EB
near junction of Robin's Lane
11 - 11 Mon - Sat, 12 - 10.30 Sun
Guest Beer (Occasional)   H
A hotel bar, open to residents and non-residents. Seating is on two levels split into smaller areas by stained-glass style partitions.

Porter Brewing Co Ltd

ROSSENDALE BREWERY

Lancashire

Real ales at unbeatable quality, value, and choice.
Mild, Floral Dance, Bitter, Rossendale Ale, Railway Sleeper, Porter, Sunshine
plus excellent seasonal & occasional ales
Hud Rake, Haslingden, Lancashire
(01706) 214021

CAMRA's National Inventory

By John Clarke

What they say: *"We have preserved its character"*
What they mean: *"We've knocked out all the walls and filled it full of junk"*

Of the 60,000 or so public houses in the whole of the UK, it is estimated that less than four per cent have been able to escape drastic alteration in recent times. The number whose interiors might be considered of **outstanding** heritage interest has dwindled to around 200 or so. The National Inventory is CAMRA's pioneering initiative for bringing greater recognition and protection to the country's most priceless historic pubs.

What then is the 'National Inventory' and what is its importance? The list of pub interiors is the culmination of 11 years work, having started life as an 'emergency initiative' to take account of the turmoil facing the brewing industry following the 1989 Beer Orders and the large-scale pub disposals by national brewers that came in their wake. The idea, then and now, has been to identify and seek safeguarding for the very best of Britain's architectural heritage of pub interiors.

Hundreds of pubs have been looked at by a team of volunteer surveyors and while many worthwhile pubs were flagged up, far fewer met the, admittedly demanding, criteria. Time and again we encountered pubs which had been seriously compromised with walls and interior fittings ripped out, sometimes replaced with reproduction 'historic' interiors, but in many cases simply victims of the refurbishments of the Sixties and Seventies when little regard was had to our architectural heritage. Often we encountered surviving fragments, perhaps even an entire room, sitting incongruously amid the neon and plastic of a later age.

The range of pubs which have made it to the list reflects the very diversity which is the backbone of the British public house tradition. Apart from the classic' gin palaces' we have also sought out plainer but still unspoilt urban and rural beerhouses. In Victorian towns and cities as much care was lavished on smaller domestic pubs as on the great gin palaces, and since these pubs have perhaps had more need to adapt and change with the times, truly unspoilt examples have proved elusive. Of particular rarity are truly unspoilt pubs from between the wars. Not only do fewer pubs date from this period but the larger 'roadhouse' style pubs have invariably been gutted over the past 20-30 years. It is in the smaller, domestic examples that the 1920s and 1930's pub survives, with such local pubs as the Nursery and the Swan With Two Necks being prime examples of this vanishing breed.

Apart from identifying the best of what is left, the National Inventory is also being used as a tool for these pubs' preservation. We have found that no more than half of the pubs identified had any form of statutory protection. Even where a pub was listed as being of historic importance, the listing description tended to concentrate on the exterior features and generally overlook what was inside, namely what made the building work as a pub. In some cases this led to the false belief that only part of a pub was protected. Exteriors were lovingly preserved while all hell broke loose inside. This now is beginning to change, with more pubs getting listed status and the descriptions of those already protected 'beefed up' to lay greater emphasis on interior details. At the same time many pub owners have shown a greater appreciation and understanding of the remaining heritage qualities of their pubs.

Stockport has one of the greatest concentrations of National Inventory pubs, with five full entries, and several others only just failing to make the grade. The 'famous five' are:

The Nursery, Green Lane, Heaton Norris. The pub is virtually as it was built in 1939 incorporating twentieth-century standards of comfort and convenience but with old-fashioned solid and durable standards of construction and a clean, spacious and unembellished design. There is generous use of light oak including full-height panelling in the lounge and the leaded glass windows are decorated with an occasional coloured glass panel depicting horticultural nursery motifs - a spade, a watering can or a flower. In addition to the large lounge there is a bar lobby area, a smoke room/dining room, a vault with a separate entrance and a function room/dining room upstairs.

The Alexandra, Northgate Road, Edgeley. Built in 1911, the Alexandra is beautifully intact. Only the back bar and the outdoor department have been altered. The entrance hall with a hatch to the bar has a dado of glazed tiles with multi-coloured Art

Nouveau motifs. A room leads off each corner of the hall. Each glazed door is etched with 'Tap Room', 'Smoke Room', 'Bar Parlour' etc. The rooms have fixed seating, lobby screens with coloured glass and original fireplaces, some with original Art Nouveau surrounds. The decoration continues up the stairs with an impressive coloured glass window on the half landing.

The Arden Arms, Millgate, Stockport. The Arden Arms has a beautifully preserved interior dating from the nineteenth century, with simple wooden panelling, bench seating and quarry tile floors. Three rooms open up off the lobby area around the bar and there is a snug which can only be accessed by passing through the bar. There have been some structural alterations in recent years (new openings, a new room formed from former living quarters and some bench seating removed) but the quality that remains is very evident.

The Swan with Two Necks, Princes Street, Stockport. Rebuilt or remodelled about 1926, this pub has not really changed since. The exterior is not a particularly elegant composition but what counts is the interior. It is simply organised with a corridor running the length of the building on the right-hand side, and leading (from front to back) a public bar, the servery (with a drinking lobby in front) and a lounge behind. Extensive use is made of wall panelling as was so often the case in inter-war pubs. The lounge, particularly, with its Tudor-style fireplace, succeeds in creating a warm, comfortable atmosphere.

The Queens Head (Turners Vaults), Little Underbank, Stockport. A three-storey building and part of a late eighteenth-century or early nineteenth-century block. It is extremely narrow and shows how many small urban pubs must have looked a hundred years ago. The furnishings are probably late Victorian. The extreme narrowness of the interior led to some rearrangement of some of the internal woodwork but this was carried out with care and the pub still retains an authentic feel. Behind the main bar are a couple of smaller ones. Make a point of having a look at a very rare survival behind the counter - taps which formerly dispensed wines and spirits.

Before thermometers were invented, brewers would dip a thumb or finger into the mix to find the right temperature for adding yeast. Too cold, and the yeast wouldn't grow. Too hot, and the yeast would die. This thumb in the beer is where "rule of thumb" comes from.

BREDBURY

ARDEN ARMS

Ashton Road, Castle Hill, SK6 2QN
by the Denton border.
11 - 11 Mon - Sat, 12 - 10.30 Sun
 Robinsons Hatters   E
 Robinsons Best Bitter   E

Despite the traffic roaring past, still has a country-pub feel. A very good pub to take young children on a nice day.

CROWN

96 Stockport Road East, SK6 2AA
junction of Crown Street
4 - 11 Mon - Thu, 12 - 11 Fri - Sat, 12 - 10.30 Sun
 Boddingtons Bitter   H

Good local pub with accent on Games. Separate lounge and games room.

GREYHOUND   A1

Lower Bents Lane, SK6 2NL
Tel: 0161 430 3682
junction of Elm Street
BR, Buses: 330 (short walk), 384 (383 return), 386
2 - 11 Mon - Fri, 12 - 11 Sat, 12 - 10.30 Sun
 Robinsons Hatters   E
 Robinsons Best Bitter   E

This dominant Victorian-style building was once a favourite watering hole for thirsty workers from Bredbury steelworks. The Mill has long since gone but the Greyhound still attracts a loyal clientele. If you get bored while sitting in the lounge bar, look up and admire the huge collection of water jugs suspended from the ceiling.

HORSFIELD ARMS   A2
Ashton Road, SK6 2QN
Tel: 0161 430 6390
opposite junction of Lingard Lane
Buses: 324
11 - 11 Mon - Sat, 12 - 10.30 Sun
Main Meals: 12 - 2 Mon - Fri
  Robinsons Hatters   E
  Robinsons Best Bitter   E
The Horsfield Arms is situated in front of Robinson's bottling plant. The pub's exterior looks unassuming, but do not be deceived by this, because inside is a cosy, comfortable and welcoming local which draws a loyal clientele of locals and office workers. The pub was named after the Horsfield family who acquired their wealth in the cotton manufacturing industry in Hyde. They bought Harden Hall Estate in the early part of the nineteenth century and maintained a presence in the area for almost a century. This pub is easy to pass by, but definitely worth stopping off for.

🍺 🚗 📷 ♣ ✂ 🍴

QUEENS
2 Higher Bents Lane, SK6 2JN
NO REAL ALE

RISING SUN
57 - 59 Stockport Road East, SK6 2AA
by Bredbury BR
12 - 11 Mon - Sat, 12 - 10.30 Sun
  Tetley Bitter   H
  John Smiths Cask Bitter   H
Has a low-ceilinged bar with plenty of rustic, beams and brasses. A beer garden exists to the rear.

SAMUEL WEBSTER
190 Redhouse Lane, SK6 2JG
NO REAL ALE

SPORTSMANS REST
99 Higher Bents Lane, SK6 2NA
junction of Harrytown
2 - 11 Mon - Fri, 12 - 11 Sat, 12 - 10.30 Sun
  Robinsons Hatters   E
  Robinsons Best Bitter   E
A popular, basic, open-plan, 'no-frills' pub. The stone exterior of this 19th century, ex-Bells Brewery house, survives.

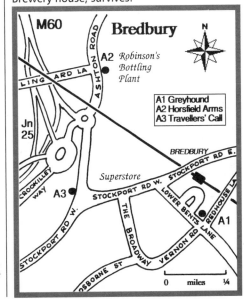

TRAVELLERS CALL A3

402 Stockport Road West, SK6 2DT
Tel: 0161 430 2511
junction of Ashton Road
Buses: 330, 384 (383 return), 386
12 - 11 Mon - Sat, 12 - 10.30 Sun
Main Meals: 12 - 2.30 & 5 - 7 Mon - Fri, 12 - 6 Sat, 12 - 5 Sun

Lees Bitter	H
Lees Seasonal Guest	H

A rare Lees outlet in Stockport, this pub was, for many years, under threat of demolition from a proposed by-pass. However, now the future looks much more secure with the brewery investing heavily to create a fine local. In addition to the regular Lees beers, their seasonal offerings are usually also available.
During the early part of the 19th Century travellers coming from the direction of Stockport were frequently the victims of local highway robbers. Nowadays the locals are of a friendlier disposition and a warm welcome is assured in this deservedly popular local.

YEW TREE

Osborne Street, SK6 2EX
NO REAL ALE

BRINNINGTON

CHESHIRE CAT
150 Middlesex Road, SK5 8HJ
by Brinnington railway station
12 - 11 Mon - Sat, 12 - 10.30 Sun

Robinsons Best Bitter	H

Swiss chalet-style appearance with a large single gable, smaller inside. Disco Fri/Sun. Note the cat tiles in the toilets and bar front.

FARMERS ARMS
Brinnington Road, SK5 8HX
NO REAL ALE

JACK & JILL
Brinnington Road, SK5 8AD
near junction of Whitebank Avenue
12 - 11 Mon - Sat, 12 - 10.30 Sun

Robinsons Hatters	E
Robinsons Best Bitter	E

Long, low building. Main room with multi-coloured wall decor, and hop-festooned, a somewhat club-like atmosphere.

> "*I FEEL SORRY FOR PEOPLE WHO DON'T DRINK. WHEN THEY WAKE UP IN THE MORNING, THAT'S AS GOOD AS THEY'RE GOING TO FEEL ALL DAY.*" - FRANK SINATRA

SO begins the famous Monty Python "Dead Parrot" sketch, perhaps one of the most quoted of all time. John Cleese certainly had a point; often we have cause to complain. The Campaign for Real Ale was formed to complain, and went on to become the most successful consumer organisation in Europe. We certainly saved traditional beer, but the fight is far from over. Bad beer, adulterated beer and short measure still trouble us on occasion.

You, the customer, are in the front line and we all know it can be all too easy to do nothing; "I don't like to make a fuss"; "No-one else is complaining""; "Perhaps it's supposed to taste like this"; "I might get barred" - the excuses for inaction are endless. Remember the point though: if you've paid good money for something which is substandard, then you've been swindled - so complain!

Once you've decided to do something, the question remains, how? Opening Times offers a few words of advice and technical points:

★ **Be Polite** - if you create a conflict, you've lost. - the licensee has home advantage!

★ **Be Discreet** - no licensee wants to draw attention to a problem

★ **Be Reasonable** - if the beer has reached the end of the barrel, you can tell at once. The landlord may not be drinking and be unaware of this.

★ **Be Diplomatic** - "I think this might have gone" is less of an insult to the cellarman's craft than "this tastes foul!"

★ **Be Sensible** - a tiny shortfall in volume isn't worth the fuss, but perhaps nearly an inch is worth a polite request to "squeeze a drop more in".

★ **Be Decisive** - bad beer should be returned promptly. Struggling valiantly through 3/4 of a pint will undermine your case.

★ **Don't** - complain to an outside body (see below) without first trying to gain satisfaction in the pub.

★ **Don't** - accept the guff that "real ale is supposed to look like oxtail soup and taste like vinegar" or that old standby "no-one else has complained". Stand your ground.

Remember that the law on "full measure" is currently something of a shambles. The head is legally part of your pint but the guidelines say that your pint should be 95% liquid and short measures should be topped up with good grace. Trading Standards officers may still be prepared to take action where these guidelines are consistently flouted.

Beer which tastes bad is "goods unfit for the purpose" under the Trades Description Act and you have a statutory right to redress. You could ask for your money back, but a replacement from another barrel is the best solution. You should be able to read the price list without binoculars or a stepladder. What do you mean "what price list?".

If you **don't** get satisfaction from the licensee, contact:

The Trading Standards Officer (for consistent short measure or missing price list)

The Environmental Health Officer (for sour beer or unhygienic practices)

The Brewery/Pub Owner - (for poor beer in a tied house or poor customer service)

The local branch of CAMRA (who will certainly check up on any horror stories)

Luckily none of the above is relevant in most of the pubs in the Opening Times area. Normally we find a full measure of good beer served by polite staff in pleasant surroundings, and that any minor niggles are dealt with in a quick and friendly manner. With your help, that's how things will stay, and we hope that the occasion on which you have to "register a complaint" are as scarce as the famous dead "Norwegian Blue Parrot".

The phone number of the Stockport Trading Standards Officers is:
0161 474 4248

CALE GREEN, EDGELEY & HEAVILEY

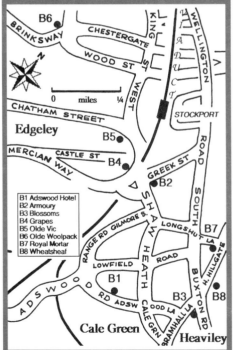

ADSWOOD HOTEL   B1

60 Adswood Lane West, SK3 8HZ
Tel: 0161 480 6086
quarter mile off junction of Shaw Heath
Buses: 309, 313, 374
12 - 11 Mon - Sat, 12 - 10.30 Sun
*Main Meals: 12 - 2 Mon - Fri, 12 - 3.30 Sat,
12 - 5 Sun*

Robinsons Hatters	E
Robinsons Best Bitter	E

Large, attractive red-brick pub set back from the road behind a cobbled courtyard in a quiet residential area. The interior has been opened out over the years and a modern bar installed, but four distinct drinking areas remain, with a welcoming atmosphere and plenty of comfortable seating. A theme of shire horses, both pottery and pictured, is evident throughout. At the rear is an extensive, secluded beer garden that comes as a surprise in this urban setting and is the ideal place to enjoy a drink on a summer evening.

---

*ALWAYS DO SOBER WHAT YOU SAID
YOU'D DO DRUNK.
THAT WILL TEACH YOU TO KEEP
YOUR MOUTH SHUT.*
-ERNEST HEMMINGWAY

Map key:
B1 Adswood Hotel
B2 Armoury
B3 Blossoms
B4 Grapes
B5 Olde Vic
B6 Olde Woolpack
B7 Royal Mortar
B8 Wheatsheaf

Edgeley
Cale Green
Heaviley

ALEXANDRA HOTEL
195 Northgate Road, SK3 9NJ
junction of Chatham Street
12 - 3 & 5.30 - 11 Mon - Fri, 12 - 11 Sat, 1 - 4
& 7.30 - 10.30 Sun
  Robinsons Best Bitter   H
  Robinsons Seasonal Guest   H
Grade-2 listed multi roomed gem on CAMRA's National Inventory of Classic Pub Interiors. Tiling and etched glass abound - the rear snug, separated from the lobby by a mahogany and stained glass partition, is a particularly fine room.

ARMOURY   B2
31 Shaw Heath, SK3 8BD
Tel: 0161 477 3711
corner of Greek Street
BR, Buses: 11, 28, 310, 368, 369, 371
11 - 11 Mon - Sat, 12 - 10.30 Sun
  Robinsons Hatters   H
  Robinsons Best Bitter   H
  Robinsons Old Tom   G
This Victorian pub was refitted in the 1920s and large segments of the interior remain largely intact since then, with a host of original fittings and prior ownership by the old Bell's Brewery still evident in the interior glasswork. The only major change has been the loss of the old off-sales, incorporated into the main lounge.
The pub contains rooms for most tastes - a bright, brassy lounge, a drinking lobby with its own bar counter, a darts room at the back and an excellent traditional vault, arguably one of the best in town. The sense of tradition is heightened by the frequent sight of a cask of the powerful Old Tom on the bar counter. Outside at the back is a new, secluded beer garden, which can be quite a sun-trap in the summer months.
The Armoury has a more mature clientele, which not only accounts for the very healthy cask ale sales, but also the absence of a juke box. Taped background music is the order of the day, enlived by occasional sing-alongs.
A good old-fashioned pub in the best sense of the word.

BAMFORD ARMS
73 Buxton Road, SK2 6NB
junction of Nangreave Road
11 - 11 Mon - Sat, 12 - 10.30 Sun
  Boddingtons Bitter   H
  Marstons Pedigree   H
  Tetley Bitter   H
A rustic-library look interior. Travel Inn attached.

> *FILL WITH MINGLED CREAM AND AMBER,*
> *I WILL DRAIN THAT GLASS AGAIN.*
> *SUCH HILARIOUS VISIONS CLAMBER*
> *THROUGH THE CHAMBERS OF MY BRAIN.*
> *QUAINTEST THOUGHTS, QUEEREST FANCIES*
> *COME TO LIFE AND FADE AWAY;*
> *WHAT CARE I HOW TIME ADVANCES?*
> *I AM DRINKING ALE TODAY*
>
> *- EDGAR ALLAN POE*

CHURCH INN
Moseley Street, SK3 9HR
junction of Bengal Street
12 - 11 Mon - Sat. 12 - 10.30 Sun

Robinsons Hatters	H
Robinsons Best Bitter	H
Robinsons Cumbria Way	H

A welcoming community local. Cask mild is now reintroduced - a rare gain!

COMFORTABLE GILL
34 King Street West, SK3 0DY
opposite Bus garage
11 - 11 Mon - Sat, 12 - 10.30 Sun

Boddingtons Bitter	H

Rambling open-plan pub with psuedo-rustic decor. Quiz nights and entertainment often feature.

BLOSSOMS B3
2 Buxton Road, SK2 6NU
Tel: 0161 477 2397
junction of Bramhall Lane
Buses: 191, 192, 199, 378
12 - 3 & 5 - 11 Mon - Fri, 12 - 11 Sat, 12 - 10.30 Sun
Main Meals: 12 - 2 Daily, 5 - 7.30 Mon - Thu

Robinsons Hatters	H
Robinsons Best Bitter	H
Robinsons Old Tom (winter)	G

Built as a coaching house in the 18th century, this four-roomed pub with lobby bar is reported to be the exit place for an escape tunnel from Bramhall Hall, and was used for the planning meetings when designing St. George's Church. Nowadays it supports two separate Lodges of the Royal Antideluvian Order of Buffaloes on Mondays and Fridays. With a warm, friendly atmosphere and excellent service this pub is well worth a visit. One of the few Stockport pubs to offer a pinball game.

BOW GARRETT
199 Higher Brinksway, SK3 0HP
NO REAL ALE

BOWLING GREEN
Charles Street, SK1 3JR
NO REAL ALE

COPPERFIELDS BAR
Adswood Lane West, SK3 8HZ
NO REAL ALE

DUKE OF YORK
113 Buxton Road, SK2 6LR
100 yards south of junction of Nangreave Rd
12 - 11 Mon - Sat, 12 - 10.30 Sun

Robinsons Best Bitter	H
Robinsons Seasonal Guest	H

Far larger than it looks with three plush rooms at the front and a two-level vault at the rear. A large beer garden with play area.

FLYING DUTCHMAN
137 Higher Hillgate, SK1 3HR
junction of Longshut Lane/Hempshaw Lane
11.30 - 11 Mon - Fri, 12 - 11 Sat, 12 - 10.30 Sun

Robinsons Hatters	E
Robinsons Best Bitter	E

Smallish pub evoking a modern style. Disco and karaoke popular on weekend evenings.

GARDENERS ARMS
72 Northgate Road, SK3 9PH
near Doris Road junction
12 - 11 Mon - Wed, 11.30 - 11 Thu - Sat, 12 - 10.30 Sun

Boddingtons Bitter	H

Large semi open-plan 1930s pub known locally as 'The War Office'. Possibly used as recruiting station in World War One.

OPENING TIMES
IS CAMRA'S DOUBLE-AWARD WINNING REGIONAL MAGAZINE COVERING STOCKPORT, CENTRAL, SOUTH AND EAST MANCHESTER, TAMESIDE, PARTS OF HIGH PEAK AND MACCLESFIELD. NEARLY 7,000 COPIES ARE DISTRIBUTED EVERY MONTH.

Distributed throughout Stockport, Central, East & South Manchester, Tameside, N.E. Cheshire & Macclesfield
Volume 19 Issue 4 — FREE CAMRA MAGAZINE — 6,700 CIRCULATED THIS MONTH — FREE

IT CAN BE PICKED UP IN MANY OF THE PUBS FEATURED IN VIADUCTS & VAULTS. OPENING TIMES IS FREE.

GRAPES — B4
1c Castle Street, SK3 9AB
Tel: 0161 480 3027
corner of Mercian Way
BR, Buses: 11, 28, 310, 368, 369, 371
11 - 11 Mon - Sat, 12 - 10.30 Sun

Robinsons Hatters	H
Robinsons Best Bitter	H

This small two room pub epitomises all that is best in the term "Local Boozer". No architectural gem but wins through by concentrating on its strengths - good beer and a great atmosphere generated by a loyal crowd of regulars. The licensees will have been there 21 years in 2003 and this continuity only adds to the enduring appeal of the pub. To enjoy the Grapes at its best, visit at lunchtime and afternoon when it's at its busiest. No food.

GREYHOUND
27 Bowden Street, SK3 9HG
junction of Moseley Street
11 - 11 Mon - Sat, 12 - 10.30 Sun

Boddingtons Bitter	H

A 1950s house with an L-shaped Lounge and small, lower-set vault. Unusual wood-framed outdoor drinking area.

After consuming a bucket or two of vibrant brew they called aul, or ale, the Vikings would head fearlessly into battle, often without armour or even shirts. In fact, "berserk" means "bare shirt" in Norse, and eventually took on the meaning of their wild battles.

HOLLYWOOD
12 Bloom Street, SK3 9LA
NO REAL ALE

JOLLY CROFTER
15 Castle Street, SK3 9AB
NO REAL ALE

JOLLY SAILOR
218 Bramhall Lane, SK3 8TE
a quarter mile south of Davenport station
12 - 11 Mon - Sat, 12 - 10.30 Sun

Boddingtons Bitter	H
Theaksons Cool Cask	H
Charles Wells Bombadier	H
Courage Directors	H

Large Scottish & Newcastle 'Steak and Ale' house. The beer range differs at times.

OLDE VIC — B5
1 Chatham Street, SK3 9ED
Tel: 0161 480 2410
behind Stockport station, junction of King Street West
BR, Buses: 11, 28, 310, 368, 369, 371
5 - 11 Mon - Fri, 7 - 11 Sat, 7 - 10.30 Sun

up to five Guest Beers	H
Westons Special Vintage (Cider)	H

The first Stockport pub to offer a changing range of guest beers and still flying the flag for choice and quality, as evidenced by the pump clip 'ceiling' above the bar. This is a tight ship affably run by larger than life licensee Steve Brannan. No swearing rules are strictly enforced but this is an easy-going pub with a warm welcome for everyone. The secluded drinking area at the back is well used in the summer, whilst a blazing real fire provides a welcome focus in winter months. The pub dog is a real softy, but the cat has a foul temper - be warned! Not much to look at from the outside but a "must" to visit.

OLDE WOOLPACK B6

70 Brinksway, SK3 0BY
Tel: 0161 476 0688
near Hollywood Way Bridge
Buses: 312
11.30 - 3 & 5 - 11 Mon - Thu, 11.30 - 11 Fri. 11.30 - 4.30 &
7.30 - 11 Sat, 12 - 10.30 Sun
Main Meals: 12 - 2 Mon - Fri, 12 - 2.30 Sat & Sun

Theakston Best Bitter	H
Theakston Cool Cask	H
Three Guest Beers	H

In the late 1980s, the Woolpack seemed des-
tined for permanent closure. Originally a
Greenalls pub, it later had a stint as a failed
freehouse then closed down with rumours of
conversion into a B&B.
Luckily the pub was taken over by Bob Dickinson
who set about restoring its fortunes and since
then it has gone from strength to strength,
majoring on quality cask ales and good home-
cooked food - both much appreciated by the
occupants of Stockport's landmark blue pyra-
mid that dwarfs the nearby pub. While there has
been some opening out, the Woolpack still retains much of the original layout of front and
rear lounges, drinking lobby and well-used vault.
The history of consistent excellence is evidenced
by the clutch of recent CAMRA awards which
adorn the walls, from Pub of the Month to Pub
of the Year, local and Regional.
The beer range consists of two or three
permanent beers, usually from the national or
larger regional brewers, complemented by a
similar number of changing guest beers, often
from micros.

PINEAPPLE

50 Castle Street, SK3 9AD
NO REAL ALE

PRINCE ALBERT

107 Castle Street, SK3 9AR
NO REAL ALE

ROYAL MORTAR B7

154 Higher Hillgate, SK1 3QT
Tel: 0161 480 5073
near junction of Longshut Lane
Buses: 191, 192, 199, 358, 378, 383
3 - 11 Mon - Fri, 11 - 11 Sat, 12 - 10.30 Sun

Robinsons Hatters	H
Robinsons Best Bitter	H

A good sized house with characterful arched
windows, behind which lie a two room pub that
has seen some alterations over the years. For a
time it had lost its way until the present licensees took control in 2001. All sorts of improve-
ments were made - decor, ambience, beer quality, which together turned the pub from a no-

hoper to a really thriving local. The front bar leads round to a comfortable lounge with many brass plates decorating the walls. The vault is at the rear and features a pool table and dart board; this latter item is very important in the life of the pub as the Mortar plays host to one of the best teams in the district - it even numbers an England national player amongst its members. Plans are afoot to utilise an adjoining property to provide inside toilets and thus enlarge the drinking area at the rear and outside. Hosts weekday disco / karaoke events and such.

🚗 ❀ ◀ 👣 ✏️

ROYAL OAK
124 Castle Street, SK3 9AL
junction of Grenville Street
11 - 11 Mon - Sat, 12 - 10.30 Sun
Holt Bitter   H
The beamed interior gives a vaguely rustic feel both in the spacious lounge and large, well-used vault.

WHEATSHEAF   B8
205 - 9 Higher Hillgate, SK1 2RB
Tel: 0161 480 0171
junction of Buxton Road
Buses: 191, 192, 199, 378
11 - 11 Mon - Sat, 12 - 10.30 Sun
Bar Snacks: Rolls 11 - 10, Main Meals: 11 - 2 Mon - Fri
Tetley Bitter   H
Marston Pedigree   H
Guest Beer   H
If you are doing a Hillgate crawl (and this is the penultimate - Christmas - pub event on CAMRA's annual calendar), the "Sheaf" provides a useful break from the Robinsons diet. A central bar with leaded glass pot shelves featuring a sheaf motif divide the pool and darts area to the left, from the dining-cum-lounge area to the right. Betwixt the two lies a drinking lobby exhibiting a gallery of hand-painted caricatures of local characters and customers - some handsome, others grotesque, but all very entertaining. An unusual event for a pub to host is a Saturday

THE PROBLEM WITH THE WORLD IS THAT EVERYONE IS A FEW DRINKS BEHIND.

-

HUMPHREY BOGART

SIR ROBERT PEEL
83 Castle Street, SK3 9AR
NO REAL ALE

SWAN
37 Shaw Heath, SK3 8BD
NO REAL ALE

TOM THUMBS
54 King St West, SK3 0DT
NO REAL ALE

A beer is NOT just a beer. All told, there are 27 different styles of beer, with a further breakdown of 49 sub styles.

karaoke AND curry, but that's the kind of mixed crowd the pub attracts. A motorcycle club also meets here on Tuesdays.

❀ ◀ 👣

WINDSORS
41 Castle Street, SK3 9AT
opposite junction of York Street
12 - 11 Mon - Sat, 12 - 10.30 Sun
Boddingtons Bitter   H
Edgeley's largest pub by far. Roadhouse in style, it reopened early 2003 after a two year closure period. Very large, smart lounge, central bar and large vault with pool. Tasteful decor of part panelling and mirrors. Live acts Fridays.

BEARTOWN BREWERY Ltd.

UNIT 9,
VAREY ROAD,
EATON BANK
TRADING ESTATE,
CONGLETON.
CW12 1UW
TEL: 01260 299964

ROBINSON'S OUR LOCAL INDEPENDENT

BY JOHN CLARKE

FREDERIC Robinson Ltd is Stockport's only independent brewer and is also one of the largest of the surviving family brewers, with an estate of about 420 pubs stretching from the Lake District to the Potteries, and from the Peak District to Anglesey.

Founded by Frederic Robinson in 1838, the company is still run by the fifth and sixth generations of the Robinson family. Indeed, only blood-line Robinsons can hold shares in the company, and it is this tight family control and involvement which has helped the company preserve its independence over the years – that plus a perhaps unfashionable but still welcome view that each generation holds the company in trust for future generations, rather than seeing it as a cash-cow for short term profit and gain. That's not to say that Robinson's has stood still over the years. Indeed, it has pursued quite an aggressive expansion programme over the years, purchasing several local brewers (the last being Hartleys of Ulverston in 1982 which followed the acquisition of local rivals Bell & Co in 1949) and numerous independent pubs, particularly in North Wales.

At the same time there has been considerable investment in the brewery, which today presents an interesting blend of old and new, and the large packaging plant behind the Horsfield Arms in Bredbury. Indeed, the large state-of-the-art Unicorn Packaging Centre now provides a healthy income stream for the company, bottling about 100 different lines for a host of companies. Long-term plans to relocate the brewery itself to this site seem to have been abandoned, although the cask beer is now tankered up to Bredbury for barrelling.

The beer range has been evolving in recent years, too. Hatters Mild has been rebadged simply 'Hatters' in an attempt to reverse the long-term decline associated with mild beer in general. A darker version, still very rare, is now being made more widely available and it is to be hoped that this elusive beer will soon have its own dedicated pump-clip. Plain 'Bitter' has been renamed 'Old Stockport' and this, too, has led to an increase in its availability. Best Bitter remains the flagship brew and of course the powerful Old Tom remains a classic of the barley wine style of beer, although these days the brewery prefers to simply call it a strong ale. A re-creation of Hartleys XB is the last surviving brand from the old Ulverston Brewery and is rarely seen locally.

Frederics is a 5% premium beer and when introduced several years ago, was the first new product from the brewery for many years. Sadly, it also remains a rarity in local Robinson's pubs. Then in 2000, a range of bi-monthly seasonal beers was introduced. This range has evolved slowly with two of the slower selling beers being dropped for the 2002-03 programme. There have also been two new permanent additions to the range. Cumbria Way was initially made as a one-off for the Ulverston Ale Trail but has proved so popular that it has been retained as a regular beer, primarily for the old Hartleys estate (although it is available to all Robinson's pubs) where its success may cast a shadow over the long-term survival of XB. Buoyed up by this success a second new beer, Snowdon Bitter, was introduced for the Welsh pubs although, again, this is available to all pubs across the estate. Relations between CAMRA and Robinson's haven't always been easy. Pub refurbishments were a particular bone of contention, and it has to be said much work carried out in the 1970s and 1980s paid too little regard to the existing fabric and heritage of too many pubs and the interior finish too often resembled airport lounges. Luckily those days are now hopefully past and, as Production Director David Robinson commented, Robinson's and CAMRA sing largely from the same hymn sheet in the pursuit of quality cask beers sold in welcoming traditional locals.

25

CHEADLE

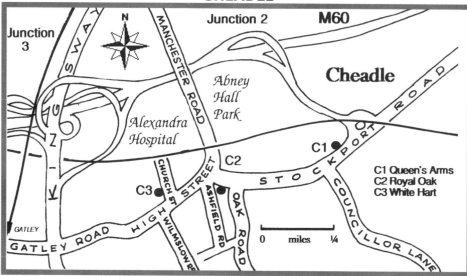

C1 Queen's Arms
C2 Royal Oak
C3 White Hart

ASHLEA
14 Manchester Road, SK8 2NP
100 yds north of High Street junction, near Abney Park
11 - 11 Mon - Sat, 12 - 10.30 Sun

Theakstons Best Bitter	H
Marstons Pedigree	H
Courage Directors	H

The current building dates from 1939 and has four small streams flowing through the cellar. An atmospheric pub, whose wide-ranging menu includes fish specialities.

BARSH
65 High Street, SK8 1BJ
11 - 11 Mon - Sat, 12 - 10.30 Sun

Boddingtons Bitter	H
Guest Beer	H

The former Vine, now a stripped-out, pared-down, blond-wood, chilled-out cafe bar. Good to see cask beer in such an establishment. Opens at 9 daily (11 Sun) for coffee and such.

CHESHIRE LINE TAVERN
Manchester Road, SK8 2NZ
half mile north of High Street junction, next to garden centre between M60 and river Mersey.
11 - 11 Mon - Sat, 12 - 10.30 Sun

Banks Bitter	H
Marstons Pedigree	H

A former station house with a single open-plan lounge. There is an extensive food menu.

CROWN
81 High Street, SK8 1AA
50 yds east of junction of Wilmslow Road
10.30 - 11 Mon - Sat, 12 - 4 & 7 - 10.30 Sun

Hydes Light	H
Hydes Bitter	H
Hydes Jekyll's Gold	H
Hydes Seasonal Guest	H

A narrow shop front exterior. Extensive range of Hydes' beers.

GEORGE & DRAGON
1 High Street, SK8 1AX
junction of Manchester Road
11 - 11 Mon - Sat, 12 - 10.30 Sun

Greenalls Bitter	H
Boddingtons Bitter	H

A former coaching inn. Popular with young clientele, emphasis on music. Pleasant rear patio in summer

MALT SHOVEL
Councillor Lane, SK8 2JE
NO REAL ALE

COME, SIT WE BY THE FIRESIDE
AND ROUNDLY DRINK WE HEAR,
TILL THAT WE SEE OUR CHEEKS ALL DYED
AND NOSES TANNED WITH BEER.
SOURCE: ROBERT HERRICK

OLD STAR INN
13 High Street, SK8 1AX
50 yds west of junction of Manchester Rd
11 - 11 Mon - Sat, 12 - 10.30 Sun

Hydes Light	H
Hydes Bitter	H
Hydes Seasonal Guest	H

A pleasant local, in a building of character - with etched glass and brewery insignia. Vault has seperate entrance.

PRINTERS ARMS
220 Stockport Road, SK8 2BT
50 yards west of M-way roundabout
11.30 - 11 Mon - Sat, 12 - 10.30 Sun

Robinsons Hatters	E
Robinsons Best Bitter	E

Smart multi-room pub with a very pleasant conservatory to the rear. This was the birthplace of the local branch of CAMRA. A friendly, family atmosphere.

Q'S WEAVERS
1 - 3 Gatley Road, SK8 1LY
NO REAL ALE

QUEENS ARMS   C1
177 Stockport Road, SK8 2DP
Tel: 0161 428 3081
junction of Councillor Lane
Buses: 11, 309, 310, 312, 371
12 - 11 Mon - Sat, 12 - 10.30 Sun

Robinsons Hatters	H
Robinsons Best Bitter	H

The small exterior is misleading. There are two small snug-type rooms flanking the front entrance which opens out onto the central bar counter area. This can become congested as the right-hand side is a dead-end corridor that

forms an impromptu stand-up drinkers area. The back room is popular with the regulars that frequent this cosy pub. Extensively modernised but retaining many original features such as bench seating, stained-glass screens, and a curious snug area formed by having a curved bar in a small room. Outdoor area for pleasant afternoons and evenings. Children welcome in a quiet "no smoking" room.

RED LION
83 Stockport Road, SK8 2AJ
1/4 mile west of Councillor Lane junction
11 - 11 Mon - Sat, 12 - 10.30 Sun

Robinsons Best Bitter	H

Traditional multi-area local, popular with a young clientele. Occasional folk sessions.

ROYAL OAK   C2
22 Stockport Road, SK8 2AA
Tel: 0161 428 3712
50 yds east of junction of Manchester Rd
Buses: 11, 309, 310, 312, 371, (45A, 130 and 157 from M/cr)
11 - 11 Mon - Sat, 12 - 10.30 Sun

Robinsons Best Bitter	H
Robinsons Seasonal Guest (occasionally)	H

Popular, often packed, local just off the Stockport end of Cheadle village. A variety of rooms and spaces provide something for everyone - from big screen football for teenagers to quieter areas for older folk. Nautical theme in some rooms, one has some very interesting model ships. Real fires, internet access, pool and even a small rear patio crammed with tables and interesting bric-a-brac.

VILLAGE HOTEL & LEISURE CLUB
Cheadle Road, SK8 1HW
NO REAL ALE

WHITE HART
C3
High Street, SK8 1PX
Tel: 0161 491 3028
opposite junction of Wilmslow Road
Buses: 11, 309, 310, 312, 371, (45A, 130 and 157 from M/cr)
11 - 11 Mon - Sat, 12 - 10.30 Sun
Main Meals: 12 - 3 Mon - Sun
Boddingtons Bitter　　　　　　　　**H**

Central to the village and beside the Parish Church, this impressive whitewashed building is part two storey, part three. The left part contains a most comfortable snug with much oak decoration - the barley-sugar twist columns and fire surround are particularly fine. This room leads to the large bar which has limited seating, but a lot of space for stand-up drinkers, needed when the pub is at its busiest. The right half of the pub is opened out with some emphasis on dining towards the rear. The decor and fittings sit well in a building of this age and character. A smallish beer garden exists between the pub and its large car park.

CHEADLE HEATH

FARMER'S ARMS
209 Stockport Road, SK3 0LX
junction of Edgeley Road.
11 - 11 Mon - Sat, 12 - 10.30 Sun
Websters Green Label　　　　　　　**H**
Morlands Old Speckled Hen　　　　　**H**

Large corner, open-plan family dining pub with pictures of local events and displays of Stockport Motor Club.

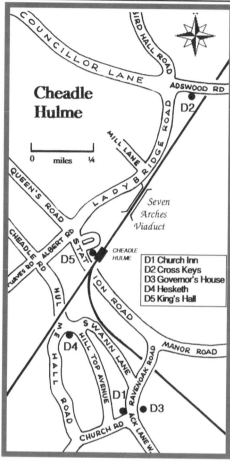

Cheadle Hulme

0 miles ¼

Seven Arches Viaduct

D1	Church Inn
D2	Cross Keys
D3	Governor's House
D4	Hesketh
D5	King's Hall

SEVEN ARCHES, CHEADLE HULME

BY MARK MCCONACHIE

Located on Ladybridge Road, this brick built structure forms part of the important West Coast mainline route via Macclesfield to the South, passing over the semi-rural tranquillity of Ladybrook Valley. Constructed in 1840-2, during the same period as Stockport's famous viaduct, it brought train services to Cheadle Hulme for the first time.

THE GUIDE TO REAL ALE IN STOCKPORT

CHEADLE HULME

CHEADLE HULME
47 Station Road, SK8 7AA
by Cheadle Hulme railway station.
11 - 11 Mon - Sat, 12 - 10.30 Sun

Holt Mild	H
Holt Bitter	H

Holt's first ever gastro-pub. Large and comfortably furnished.

CONWAY
Turves Road, SK8 6AJ
opposite junction of Conway Road
12 - 11 Mon - Sat, 10.30 - 11 Sun

Hydes Bitter	H
Hydes Jekyll's Gold	H
Hydes Seasonal Guest	H

Acquired by Hydes in 2002. Major refurbishment due as guide goes to press.

CHURCH INN   D1
90 Ravenoak Road, SK8 7EG
Tel: 0161 485 1897
junction of Church Road and Ack Lane
BR, Buses: 313 (157 from M/cr and Cheadle)
11 - 11 Mon - Sat, 12 - 10.30 Sun
Main Meals: 11.30 - 2.30, 5.30 - 8pm daily

Robinsons Hatters	H
Robinsons Old Stockport	H
Robinsons Best Bitter	H

Gives the air of a country cottage, with its low setting behind a neat hedge and well-tended front garden. Claims to be Cheadle Hulme's oldest pub, so the low-ceilinged, wood-panelled front bar rooms fit perfectly with the bucolic charm. Brass and copper in the form of plates and horseshoes adorn this cosy space. Whatever time of day, you will invariably find a few groups of people chatting and drinking amiably around the bar; attracts a more staid clientele than some local pubs, perhaps. Edwardo's Restaurant occupies the rear room, though this doubles as a lounge when non-dining. A spartan vault completes the picture.

CROSS KEYS   D2
10 Adswood Road, SK8 5QA
Tel: 0161 482 8778
near junction of Ladybridge Road
Buses: 309, 310, 313, 368, 369
11 - 11 Mon - Sat, 12 - 10.30 Sun
Bar Snacks: At all times; Main Meals: 12 - 2 & 6 - 8 Mon - Thu

Hydes Mild	H
Hydes Bitter	H

Originally a coaching house, built circa 1840, this recently refurbished pub has two rooms, one of which is a vault with large screen TV for football. The other gives the impression of being three distinctly separate and characterful rooms. The pub supports a very successful bowling team with a fine bowling green adjacent to the pub. It also boasts Italian food, home made from fresh ingredients by the resident Italian chef. With a warm, friendly atmosphere and excellent service this pub is well worth a visit.

29

GOVERNOR'S HOUSE   D3

43 Ravenoak Road, SK8 7EQ
Tel: 0161 488 4222 Fax 0161 486 1850
Junction of Ack Lane and Church Road
BR, Buses: 313 (157 from M/cr and Cheadle)
11.30 - 11 Mon - Sat, 12 - 10.30 Sun
Bar Snacks: 12 - 9 Mon - Sat, Main Meals: 12 - 2 Mon - Sat, Carvery 12 - 7 Sun, 6 - 9 Mon - Sat

Kimberley Best Bitter	H
Kimberley Seasonal Beer	H
Boddingtons Bitter	H

Formerly the Ravenoak Hotel, then via Yates' it became Hardys & Hansons only outlet in Metro Stockport in late 2000. Effectively, a large house, much extended, set in its own grounds (now mainly outdoor drinking and parking areas). Much use of dark wood, panelling, screens, bold colour, fine arts and tasteful furnishings give an air of taste and grandeur. No specific rooms exist per se, but the careful placement of screens and the use of height to good effect, divide the space up very well. Always busy, and at weekends to the point of bursting. Excellent very popular food menu .

GREYHOUND

169 Ladybridge Road, SK8 5PL
Junction of Councillor Lane
12 - 11 Mon - Sat, 12 - 10.30 Sun

Boddingtons Bitter	H

This is a 50s built roadhouse. Quite a large pub, with prominent darts, two pool tables, table football and raised seating.

HESKETH TAVERN   D4

63 Hulme Hall Road, SK8 6JZ
Tel: 0161 485 3216
third of a mile from junction of Albert Road
BR, Buses: 368, 369 (130 and 157 from M/cr and Cheadle)
11 - 11 Mon - Sat, 12 - 10.30 Sun
Main Meals: 12 - 2 Mon - Fri

John Smiths Cask Bitter	H
Two Guest Beers	H

A half-shingled, twin-gabled property named in honour of the Hesketh family. It comprises a bar, with food servery to the left, and two large raised drinking areas - front and rear - both with high, button-backed seating corralling their defined areas. The overall effect is 'Brewer's plush' with only

the odd period photo of the local area marking this pub out from what could be quite a humdrum affair. A popular quiz night is held every Monday and one Tuesday per month, and a function room is available for hire. Up to two guest ales can be available, but don't depend on it. A footpath to the south-eastern side of the railway bridge provides a useful short cut (under five minutes walk) to Station Road and the BR station.

KENILWORTH
Cheadle Road, SK8 5DX
quarter mile from junction of Albert Road
11.30 - 11 Mon - Sat, 12 - 10.30 Sun
Two Guest Beers	H

John Barras branded pub, with live sports on big screen. Changing guest beers.

KINGS HALL   D5
11 - 13 Station Road, SK8 5AF
Tel: 0161 482 0460
150 yards from the junction of Albert Road
BR, Buses: 313, 368, 369 (157 from M/cr and Cheadle)
11 - 11 Mon - Sat, 12 - 10.30 Sun
Main Meals: 11 - 10 Daily
Boddingtons Bitter	H
Shepherd Neame Spitfire	H
Guest Beers	H

A former village hall (built 1937), then a Chinese restaurant, this was converted by J.D.Wetherspoon and has been an instant success. A double-height entrance works to good effect with a curved, panelled staircase leading to a small mezzanine drinking area. Going back, you encounter the bar; a lower sofa area, then a further two tiers of tabled areas, the last of these being the no-smoking "family area" (till 9p.m.) featuring booths and large feature fireplace. This last area was created from the former beer garden when the pub was extensively altered in 2000 following a very serious fire. The pub seems extremely popular with all age groups, especially at weekends when it is just so busy you wonder if it is worth standing five deep to get served!!

MARCH HARE
Mill Lane, SK8 5PG
off Ladybridge Road
11 - 11 Mon - Sat, 12 - 10.30 Sun
Draught Bass	H
Tetley Bitter	H
Guest Beer	H

Within sight of the Seven Arches Viaduct. A plush rustic interior incorporating vintage photographs. Heavy emphasis on dining.

MICKER BROOK
Councillor Lane, SK8 5NU
NO REAL ALE

MILLINGTON HALL
67 Station Road, SK8 7AA
11 - 11 Mon - Sat, 12 - 10.30 Sun
Hydes Bitter	H

Opening early 2003, Millington Hall is one of Cheadle Hulme's most Historic buildings, expected to be given the 'heritage' treatment by Hydes.

SMITHY
Grove Lane, SK8 7NE
junction of Gillbent Road
11 - 11 Mon - Thu, 11 - 12 Fri - Sat, 12 - 11 Sun
Boddingtons Bitter	H
Theakstons Cool Cask	H

Vibrant in decor and custom, it appeals to a young audience. Largely open plan.

Interior detail of the Arden Arms, Stockport Town Centre, showing the glassed-in bar and tiling. The pub features in CAMRA's National Inventory
- for further details see page 13

COMPSTALL & MARPLE BRIDGE

HARE AND HOUNDS
19 Mill Brow, SK6 5LW
off Glossop Road and Ley Lane
5.30 - 11 Mon - Sat, 12 - 3 & 7 - 10.30 Sun

Robinsons Hatters	H
Robinsons Best Bitter	H

Secluded comfortable pub in lovely rural surroundings at the end of Mill Brow. In good foothill walking country close to Mellor Church.

LANE ENDS INN
2 Ley Lane, SK6 5DD
junction of Glossop Road
4 - 11 Mon - Thu, 12 - 11 Fri - Sat, 12 - 10.30 Sun

Adnams Broadside	H
Tetley Bitter	H

Nicely renovated open-plan pub with split levels. Good food available at lunchtimes.

MATTEO'S (ROCK TAVERN)
Glossop Road, SK6 5RX
two miles north east of Compstall Road junction
12 - 11 Mon - Sat, 12 - 10.30 Sun

Holt Bitter	H
Theakstons Bitter	H
Marstons Pedigree	H

Well appointed comfortable hotel and restaurant in a pleasant rural area with good view over Werneth Low.

ANDREW ARMS   E1
George Street, SK6 5JD
Tel: 0161 427 2281
off Compstall Brow
Buses: 383, 384
11.30 - 11 Mon - Sat, 12 - 10.30 Sun
Main Meals: 12 - 2 Daily

Robinsons Hatters	H
Robinsons Best Bitter	H

Compact, detached, stone-built pub situated just off the main road in a quiet part of this attractive village. It is popular with both locals, and visitors to the nearby Etherow Country Park, which offers wildlife and river valley walks. The interior comprises a small traditional games room and a comfortable lounge featuring a real fire in winter. Good food is served at lunchtimes including home-made curries. It has a long-serving licensee and the pub has consistently featured in CAMRA's national Good Beer Guide since the mid-1970s.

GEORGE
1 Compstall Road, SK6 5HH
by Compstall Bridge
11.30 - 11 Mon - Sat, 12 - 10.30 Sun

Robinsons Hatters	H
Robinsons Best Bitter	H

Open-plan pub in pleasant location close to the Etherow Nature Reserve. Fri/Sat live music. Bowling Green.

MIDLAND
26 Brabyns Brow, SK6 5DT
NO REAL ALE

NORFOLK
2 Town Street, SK6 5DS
NO REAL ALE

NORTHUMBERLAND ARMS   E2
64 Compstall Road, SK6 5HD
Tel: 0161 427 0211
junction of Cote Green Lane
Buses: 383, 384
2 - 11 Mon - Fri, 12 - 11 Sat, 12 - 10.30 Sun

Robinsons Hatters	H
Robinsons Best Bitter	H

Solid-looking house fronting an old paved forecourt. A smart, tiled vestibule leads through a movie poster-clad corridor to the rear positioned bar where a delightful stained glass window greets the visitor with a splendid depiction of the pub's coat of arms. Much of the decor can justifiably be described as a feast for the senses, including the pool room where every inch of wall space is taken up by framed posters, cartoons and

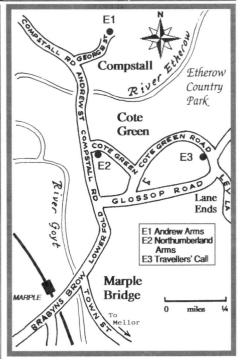

E1
Compstall
Etherow Country Park

Cote Green

E2   E3

Lane Ends

E1 Andrew Arms
E2 Northumberland Arms
E3 Travellers' Call

Marple Bridge

To Mellor

0   miles   ¼

advertisements; the comfy front lounge which benefits from a coal fire and slightly more mainstream wall decoration; and the connecting, well-used darts room. Add to all of this, mirrors, brass and copperware, Islay malts and an old clocking-in machine and you have quite a spectacle. To the side of the pub is an attractive beer garden boasting an outside service facility and for those tempted by cocktails, 150 are said to be offered!

ROYAL SCOT
48 Town Street, SK6 5AA
12 - 11 Mon - Fri, 11 - 11 Sat, 12 - 10.30 Sun

Robinsons Hatters	H
Robinsons Best Bitter	H
Robinsons Seasonal Guest	H

Comfortable open-plan pub in the centre of Marple Bridge. Robinsons first ever tied house.

SPRING GARDENS
89 Compstall Road, SK6 5HE
near Edward Street junction
12 - 3 & 5.30 - 11 Mon - Sat, 12 - 3 & 7 - 10.30 Sun

Boddingtons Bitter	H

Large open-plan pub popular with all age groups.

TRAVELLERS CALL   E3
134 Glossop Road, SK6 5EL
Tel: 0161 427 4169
opposite junction of Ley Lane
Buses: 394 (limited Mo-Sa daytime service only), ex Hazel Grove and Marple.
12 - 11 Mon - Fri, 12 - 10.30 Sun

Robinsons Hatters	H
Robinsons Best Bitter	H
Robinsons Frederics	H

Immaculate, little, end of terrace stone pub, giving clear views over verdant fields to central Marple Bridge and Mellor. An L-shaped lounge with corner bar forms the main focus for the

local patrons, with old photos of local scenes and match-boarded wainscot panelling providing much of the understated decor. A separate games room (known to locals as the 'Piano Room' - which, not surprisingly, contains an upright in there) plays host to regular darts events and also provides a modicum of privacy and some most welcome overflow seating. A small outside drinking yard lies to the rear.

WINDSOR CASTLE

I Glossop Road, SK6 5EJ
junction of Lower Fold
12 - 2 & 4 - 11 Mon - Wed, 12 - 11 Thu - Sat, 12 - 10.30 Sun

Robinsons Hatters	H
Robinsons Best Bitter	H

This large stone-built pub has a beer garden with good views. Open-plan local catering for all tastes.

EDGELEY

(SEE UNDER CALE GREEN, EDGELEY AND HEAVILEY PAGE 20)

A MEAL OF BREAD, CHEESE AND BEER CONSTITUTES THE CHEMICALLY-PERFECT FOOD
- QUEEN ELIZABETH I

THE STOCKPORT BEER & CIDER DRINKERS ANNUAL EXPERIENCE

BY JIM FLYNN

Stockport beer & Cider Festival was described in the last edition of Viaducts and Vaults as being the "longest bar in Stockport".

IN the intervening years, with more guest ales appearing on the bars of Stockport's pubs, and with these same pubs winning Greater Manchester Regional and National Pub of the Year Awards, it might be asked - does Stockport really need its own Beer and Cider Festival? Indeed, the question isn't unique to Stockport and is one that may be asked of many CAMRA festivals.

The hundreds and thousands of imbibers who visit CAMRA festivals across the UK each year (four thousand at Stockport alone), supply the answer, and it is a resounding "YES". The inference is that CAMRA festivals provide something that you just can't get down the pub. However, defining this quality is more difficult and will clearly vary from customer to customer.

For many festival goers, it will be the opportunity to sample a wide range of different beers and ciders which cannot normally be found at their local pub. During the course of a typical Stockport beer festival, around 90 different beers and dozens of ciders

Stockport's 17th

Beer & CIDER FESTIVAL

STOCKPORT TOWN HALL
29TH-31ST MAY 2003

and perries will be sold. Alternatively, many drinkers enjoy the unique atmosphere generated at a beer festival which can vary substantially from the more intimate cosiness found in the best traditional locals. At Stockport, the majestic décor of the Town Hall itself creates a grandiose ambience all of its own. Add to this the aural delights and energy provided by the musicians, the buzz and bustle of happy toppers and the distractions of the assorted stalls and you have an experience which sets Stockport Beer and Cider festival apart from a trip to the pub. If further proof of the success of unusual beer festival activities was needed, you only have to track the attendances at the Friday lunchtime sessions, which have risen steeply since the Mighty Wurlitzer Organ was first introduced for the delectation of attendees (It should be stressed that the organist falling off his stool and

breaking a limb was not a planned part of the entertainment and is not intended to be repeated!).

In contrast, how do you cater for those customers who primarily want a quiet pint and only occasionally savour the more vibrant type of atmosphere? is a difficult issue for festivals such as Stockport, which are held in one large hall. However, the festival organisers have managed to come up with several solutions, namely keeping Saturday lunchtimes as quiet sessions (i.e. without music), no evening entertainment before 8.30pm, and also at this time converting the separate family room into a "Quiet Room" for those who merely want to hear the hum of conversation.

If you want to try the beer, cider, perry and atmosphere of the Annual Stockport Beer and Cider festival come and visit us this year.

The Festival is held at the end of May/beginning of June each year, on the Thursday to Saturday following the Bank Holiday.

GATLEY & HEALD GREEN

BEECH TREE
128 Outwood Road, SK8 3LZ
NO REAL ALE

CHEADLE ROYAL
Royal Crescent, Wilmslow Road, SK8 3FE
NO REAL ALE

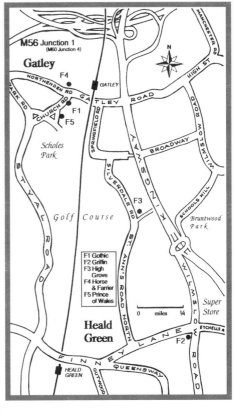

GOTHIC BAR AND GRILL   F1
61a Church Road, SK8 4NG
Tel: 0161 491 1966
near Gatley Green
**BR (from M/cr or Airport), Buses: 11, 371
(45A from M/cr and Cheadle)
12 - 11 Mon - Sat, 12 - 10.30 Sun**
Main Meals: 12 - 2 Mon - Fri

Cains Mild	H
Cains Bitter	H
Cains Formidable	H
Guest Beer	H

This pub, converted from a Methodist Church, is Cains first tied house outside its Merseyside heartland. Dating back to 1841, Gothic Bar is of unmistakably ecclesiastical origin with its high pointed roof and tall chapel-like windows. The single room interior has the bar along one side of the main hall, a raised seating area and a small upstairs balcony with dart board, where events in the pub can be viewed with ease. Good value meals are served lunchtimes and the pub has enthusiastic darts nights (Tuesday) and Quiz nights (Wednesday).

SOMETIMES WHEN I REFLECT BACK ON ALL THE BEER I DRINK I FEEL ASHAMED. THEN I LOOK INTO THE GLASS AND THINK ABOUT THE WORKERS IN THE BREWERY AND ALL OF THEIR HOPES AND DREAMS. IF I DIDN'T DRINK THIS BEER, THEY MIGHT BE OUT OF WORK AND THEIR DREAMS WOULD BE SHATTERED. THEN I SAY TO MYSELF, 'IT IS BETTER THAT I DRINK THIS BEER AND LET THEIR DREAMS COME TRUE THAN TO BE SELFISH AND WORRY ABOUT MY LIVER '

- JACK HANDY DEEP THOUGHTS

GRIFFIN   F2
124 Wilmslow Road, SK8 3BE
Tel: 0161 437 1596
junction of Finney Lane
**Buses: 312, 368, 369 (130 from M/cr, Cheadle
and Cheadle Hulme)**
12 - 11 Mon - Sat, 12 - 10.30 Sun
Bar Snacks: At all times, Main Meals: 12 - 2 Mon - Fri

Holt Mild	H
Holt Bitter	H
Holt Seasonal Guest	H

There has been a pub on this site for some 120
years. The current building dates from the
1960's and boasts a quiet snug, lounge and
separate vault, with original Victorian and Ed-
wardian photographs. The vault also has a fine
collection of circa 1930's postcard type pictures

of mainly sporting events. Huge bright red and
gold griffin carved relief on rear wall. With some
of the cheapest beer in the area, live entertainment on Thursdays and occasionally Sundays,
this thriving pub is well worth a visit for its pleasant atmosphere and excellent service.

HEALD GREEN HOTEL
Finney Lane, SK8 3QH
near junction of Styal Road
11 - 11 Mon - Sat, 12 - 10.30 Sun

Tetley Bitter	H

Large double-fronted, post-war roadhouse with
Travel Inn attached. The lounge is solely for dining with the public bar as the focus for the
drinker. Comfortable mix of carpeted and bare-
boarded areas.

HIGH GROVE   F3
Silverdale Road, SK8 4RF
Tel: 0161 428 2845 Fax 0161 428 1066
*from Gatley station via Springfield Road,
Foxdale Road then right onto Silverdale Road*
**Buses: 312 (alight top of Schools Hill, turn right
onto Kingsway, first left onto footpath (unlit)
after bus stop)**
12 - 11 Mon - Sat, 12 - 10.30 Sun
Main Meals: 12 - 2 Mon - Sat, 12 - 7 Sun

Hydes Dark Mild	H
Hydes Bitter	H
Hydes Jekyll's Gold	H
Hydes Seasonal Guest	H

The High Grove was extensively refurbished in
1999 transforming the pub into a pleasant
lounge bar with separate restaurant; much has
been made of the pub's mahogany bar and traditional styling, creating a pleasant urban pub
with a distinctive country feel. The pub can be
difficult to find as it is tucked away in the centre
of a large housing estate between Gatley and
Heald Green. Its concessions to the 21st century
are the availability of a cash machine and Internet
access in the pub. Good quality meals and bar
snacks are available daily (including Vegetarian
options). With a strong community following the
High Grove offers its wide age ranged clientele
Quiz nights, Charity events and Brewery trips,
Happy Hour is 3pm - 5pm Weekdays.

> *In English pubs, ale was ordered
> by the pints and quart.
> So in old England, when customers
> got unruly, the bartender would
> yell at them to mind their own
> pints and quarts and settle down.
> It's where we get the phrase
> "mind your P's and Q's".*

HORSE AND FARRIER F4

144 Gatley Road, SK8 4AB
Tel: 0161 428 2080
junction of Church Road
**BR (from M/cr or Airport), Buses: 11, 371
(45A from M/cr and Cheadle)**
11 - 11 Mon - Sat, 12 - 10.30 Sun
Main Meals: 12 - 2.30 & 5 - 9 Mon - Sat, 12 - 5 Sun

Hydes Light	H
Hydes Bitter	H
Hydes Jekyll's Gold	H
Hydes Seasonal Guest	H

Pub recently refurbished to a high standard as a Hydes Heritage inn. The Tudor exterior leads to a low-ceilinged multi-roomed traditional pub with restaurant. A central bar serves all the rooms there, with the Martingale Room (up-stairs) available for functions. A wide choice of food is available from snacks to steaks with the house speciality being a choice of gourmet sau-sages and mash. Vegetarian meals are also pro-vided. Very much the focal point of the village, this excellent pub is popular with all ages, chil-dren are welcome until 9pm if accompanied by a responsible adult.

Many years ago in England, pub frequenters had a whistle baked into the rim or handle of their ceramic cups. When they needed a refill, they used the whistle to get some service. "Wet your whistle" is the phrase inspired by this practice

PRINCE OF WALES F5

Gatley Green, SK8 4NF
Tel: 0161 491 0796
off Church Road
BR (from M/cr or Airport), Buses: 11, 371 (45A from M/cr and Cheadle)
11.30 - 11 Mon - Sat, 12 - 10.30 Sun
Main Meals: 12 - 2 Mon - Fri

Hydes Mild	H
Hydes Bitter	H

This delightful pub overlooking the village green was originally two cottages and this gives a clue to its main two room layout. The low ceilings give the pub a country feel complementing its bench seating and subdued lighting. In summer one can sit outside on the wooden benches over-looking the Green. On entering the pub the room on the left is the vault/tap room with darts, domi-noes and TV whilst the room on the right is the larger lounge. The pub is scheduled for a refur-bishment sometime in the near future.

RED LION

63 Church Road, SK8 4ES
NO REAL ALE

SHOCK! HORROR! A GLIMPSE
OF THE FUTURE? By ALASTAIR L. WALKER

TRY this simple experiment. Take a can of mass-market, widget-containing, smoothflow, so-called stout and pour it into a clean, empty pint glass. Go and read a book, take a walk or play a game of chess and by that time the Vesuvius-like artificial head should have subsided. Unless you actually like cloying, sweet, thin, insipid brown ales, carefully pour this ersatz stout down the sink. Without cleaning the glass, select a bottle of your favourite, reliable, normally well-behaved, bottle-conditioned beer and pour it into the same container. Marvel at the eruption of smooth, creamy, fake head that now fills the glass, with about half an inch of liquid beer struggling at the bottom. Dispose of the contents of the glass as you think fit then repeat the process. You will discover that the original invasive foam will re-appear with diminishing vigour for at least 3-4 refills. What is the reason for this not so natural phenomenon? It doesn't take a rocket scientist to figure out that the powerful chemical heading agents liberally applied to the original mass market stout are the culprits.

It is not just mega brand stouts that suffer from this affliction. Most of the keg, smoothflow, and sadly, cask, near beer products from the big brewers are now designed and manufactured by accountants and industrial chemists, ensuring that they are now an unpleasant concoction of chemical heading foam, brightening agents, sweeteners, anti-oxidants, preservatives, etc., etc. Not only is it potentially damaging to your well-being, it is extremely hazardous to your pocket. The reason for this toxic onslaught is to make a poor, lifeless, tasteless product appear to be something that it is not, so that this cheap, industrial scale pap can make huge profits for the fat cats and their ravenous shareholders at the mega- keggeries.

Of course, chemical crutches alone are not enough to shore up these dire charlatans and this is where the enormous advertising budgets of the mega brewers come into play. Have you noticed that modern adverts for these pretend beers never actually contain anything that relates to the actual product itself. Instead we get talking horses, penguins, cardboard cutouts, kung fu, gangsters, brain-dead laddish morons, etc. In fact, anything at all except a quality that actually relates to beer. There is a good reason for this. If the advert makers were instructed to concentrate solely on the desirable qualities and wholesomeness of the megabrand products, then they would be compelled to create the shortest adverts in the history of the universe.

And what is the point of the preceding tirade against the multi-national brewers and their pub co allies who force these unpleasant, over-priced mutants on to the largely unsuspecting public? Simply this;

every time that you buy a pint of artificial beer from these corporate, soul-less tyrants, you drive another nail into the coffins of the small, independent, family-owned and micro breweries who cannot compete with the financial muscle of the multi-national, relentless juggernauts, but who nevertheless still try to brew honest, wholesome, tasty, properly-brewed, good-value products. If something is not done soon, then very shortly the craft brewers and their quality products will cease to exist.

How do we stop this horrifying vision of the future from coming to pass? Stop being so lazy! Stop being so undiscerning! If your local pub or pretend free-house only sells mass market rubbish, then ask the licensee to stock some decent beers from small brewers. If they say that they are restricted by their suppliers, then ask them to put pressure on their suppliers to provide alternatives required by customer demand. Similarly, with your local off licence. Ask them to get rid of some of the high profile, low quality mega brands and replace them with interesting, flavoursome, bottle-conditioned beers. Vote with your feet! Walk/bicycle/bus/train that extra distance to drink the small brewers offerings.

The British are famous the world over for supporting and championing the cause of the underdog. Well, now the small brewer underdogs really have got their backs against the wall and are struggling to survive. They need the might of the great British beer drinking public to flex their muscles, get behind the small British brewers, and see off the largely foreign-owned Frankenstein beer monsters that are threatening our traditions and heritage!

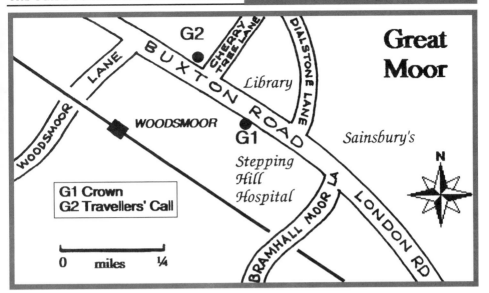

G2

Great Moor

Library

WOODSMOOR

G1

Sainsbury's

Stepping Hill Hospital

G1 Crown
G2 Travellers' Call

0 miles ¼

N

GREAT MOOR

CROWN HOTEL G1
416 Buxton Road, SK2 7JQ
Tel: 0161 483 4913
junction of Islington Road
BR (Woodsmoor), Buses:, 191, 192, 199
11.30 - 3 & 5 - 11 Mon - Fri, 11 - 11 Sat, 12 - 10.30 Sun
Main Meals: 12 - 2 Mon - Fri

Robinsons Hatters	H
Robinsons Best Bitter	H

Imposing, three-gabled house set back slightly from the road. Two large, well-furnished rooms (one with large TV for football) at the front, are divided from the curved bar by a fine, carved staircase. Some period features remain, such as etched Crown windows, panelling and tiling; the latter tiles, featuring a crown atop an escutcheon, enhance the modern bar counter. The modern archways are a touch incongruous, but the room layouts remain. The wooden screen that hides the entrance to the Gents is an unusual relic. For the sporting, a good bowling green can be found at the back whilst, back inside and through a Gothic arch, lurks a vividly-coloured pool room.

DOG AND PARTRIDGE
272 Buxton Road, SK2 7AN
opposite junction of Alldis Street
12 - 11 Mon - Sat, 12 - 10.30 Sun

Robinsons Hatters	H
Robinsons Best Bitter	H
Robinsons Seasonal Guest	H
Robinsons Old Tom (winter)	H

Terraced pub. With varied decor of tartan and wood panels in many rooms; has quite a country club feel to it. Large beer garden and play area.

> *IN HEAVEN THERE IS NO BEER...*
> *THAT'S WHY WE DRINK OURS HERE -*
> *TRADITIONAL IRISH TOAST*

39

TRAVELLERS CALL

G2

351 Buxton Road, SK2 7NL
Tel: 0161 456 6550
junction of Cherry Tree Lane
BR (Woodsmoor), Buses:, 191, 192, 199
11.30 - 11 Mon - Sat, 12 - 10.30 Sun

Robinsons Hatters	E
Robinsons Best Bitter	E
Robinsons Old Tom	G

This is a small and, seemingly, always busy three roomer. A most striking feature of the decor is a vast collection of brass nauticalia and bells. As well as the ships' bells and hand bells, there are port-holes, propellers, lanterns and telescopes. The TV and Darts room remains free of this style, whilst the front snug has a well-stocked fish tank set amidst the chimney breast. Outside, one finds a small beer garden, bizarrely furnished with a red telephone box, traffic lights and a well, surmounted by a giant red bell - all highly entertaining. The pub is also notable for its fundraising, £58,000 has been collected in 16 years by means of a ten-mile annual walk. Note the old Stockport boundary marker outside on the Cherry Tree corner.

HAZEL GROVE VIADUCT

BY MARK MCCONACHIE

Lying to the extreme south of the town and crossing Macclesfield Road between the Rising Sun pub and the terminus of the 192 bus, this 13 arch, curved, blue-brick viaduct carries passenger rail and freight to Buxton, Chinley and south-eastward. Opened to traffic in May 1857, when the town was still called Bullock Smithy prior to renaming by its more gentille Victorian inhabitants in an attempt to cover up the rather boisterous reputation of the place in those days, the viaduct is a fairly work-a-day structure that goes mostly unnoticed by passers by, probably due to its dark colouring blending in with the background.

WITHOUT QUESTION, THE GREATEST INVENTION IN THE HISTORY OF MANKIND IS BEER.

OH, I GRANT YOU THAT THE WHEEL WAS ALSO A FINE INVENTION, BUT THE WHEEL DOES NOT GO NEARLY AS WELL WITH PIZZA.

-DAVE BARRY'S BAD HABITS

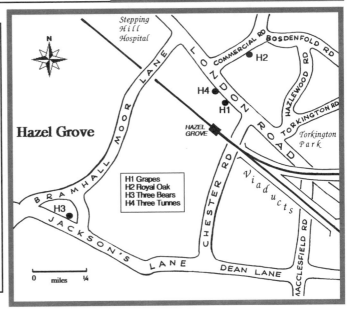

HAZEL GROVE

ANCHOR INN
62 London Road, SK7 4AF
junction of Brewers Green
12 - 11 Mon - Sat, 12 - 10.30 Sun

Robinsons Hatters	E
Robinsons Best Bitter	E
Robinsons Old Tom (winter)	H

Muted nautical theme with photos, ship's wheel, even a figurehead of a Turk. Wednesday themed curry nights. Extensive menu available weekday lunchtimes and on Sundays.

BIRD IN HAND
117 - 119 London Road, SK7 4HH
50 yards south of junction of Commercial Road
11 - 11 Mon - Sat, 12 - 10.30 Sun

Robinsons Hatters	E
Robinsons Best Bitter	E
Robinsons Seasonal Guest	E

Small L-shaped pub with old photos and prints of Stockport landmarks. Plenty of brass and copper goblets.

BROWNS CAFE BAR
281 London Road, SK7 4PS
NO REAL ALE

BULLS HEAD
341 London Road, SK7 4PS
junction of Torkington Road
11.30 - 11 Mon - Thu, 11.30 - midnight Fri - Sat, 12 - 10.30 Sun

John Smiths Bitter	H
Occasional Guest Beers	H

Large one-roomed pub with mixed clientele through the week but thronging with under 25s Thursday to Saturday nights.

COCK HOTEL
120 London Road, SK7 4DJ
junction of Commercial Road
12 - 11 Mon - Sat, 12 - 10.30 Sun

Robinsons Hatters	H
Robinsons Best Bitter	H

Two small low-beamed rooms separated by central bar. Spacious lounge. Small beer garden to rear. Note antique doors to cellar and furniture in the vault (the table was built for 'laying out' corpses).

FIVEWAYS
Macclesfield Road, SK7 6BE
junction of Dean Lane
11 - 11 Mon - Sat, 12 - 10.30 Sun

Guest Beer	H

A wedge shaped roadhouse in a sparsely pubbed part of town. Decor plush, semi open with some raised areas. The guest beer changes weekly, live Jazz in the function room on Wednesdays.

GEORGE AND DRAGON
14 London Road, SK7 4AH
NO REAL ALE

HORSE AND JOCKEY
201 London Road, SK7 4HJ
NO REAL ALE

GRAPES   H1
196 London Road, SK7 4DQ
Tel: 0161 483 4479
BR, Buses: 191, 192, 199
11.30 - 11 Mon - Sat, 12 - 10.30 Sun

| Robinsons Hatters | H |
| Robinsons Best Bitter | H |

Reputed to be Hazel Grove's oldest pub, the Grapes retains a lot of its original charm. The vault, accessible from the porch, runs the full length of the pub and is home to the dartboard, TV and Juke Box. The lounge has three distinct areas including the H.G. room dedicated to Hazel Grove Brass Band (who drink here), with pictures of old Hazel Grove and an aquarium. The Norbury Room houses a trophy cabinet and photos of the local cricket and Sunday football teams.

GROVE
53 London Road, SK7 4AX
opposite junction of Brewers Green
12 - 11 Mon - Sat, 12 - 10.30 Sun

| Robinsons Hatters | H |
| Robinsons Best Bitter | H |

Large lounge separated by three arches: viaduct to vault! Local scenes of old Stockport and black and white tiling around bar area. Geometric, comfortable snug with Mcr City memorabilia. A Bell's Brewery mosaic is still visible in the vestibule tiles.

RISING SUN
Buxton Road, SK7 6AD
junction of Macclesfield Road (192 terminus)
12 - 11.30 Mon - Sat, 12 - 10.30 Sun

John Smiths Bitter	H
Courage Directors	H
Two Guest Beers	H

Local landmark, a coaching inn dating from 1754. Attractive exterior, but frequently altered inside. Low ceilings and attractive wooden fireplace, games room, lounge and big screen area.

ROYAL OAK   H2
104 Commercial Road, SK7 4BP
Tel: 0161 483 3121
1/4 mile east off London Road
Buses: 191, 192, 199
1 - 11 Mon - Fri, 11.30 - 11 Sat, 12 - 10.30 Sun

Robinsons Hatters	H
Robinsons Best Bitter	H
Robinsons Old Tom (Winter)	H

Dating from the 1930's, this pub has recently been refurbished but retains many original features, including a splendid oak-panelled staircase. The pub has a Games room containing two pool tables, a non-smoking lounge, public bar and attractive outside seating area complete with crown bowling green. It appeals to all types of clientele, with Karaoke and occasional local D.J. The Cage at Lyme Park can be seen from the upstairs window in the pub.

until 8.30 pm. It has a disabled toilet and full level access for wheelchair users. There is a small outside drinking area at the front of the pub.

THREE BEARS   H3
Jackson's Lane, SK7 5JH
Tel: 0161 439 0611
on A5143 near junction of Dorchester Rd
Buses: 374 (alight Bramhall Moor Lane, jct. of Dorchester Road)
11 - 11 Mon - Sat. 12 - 10.30 Sun
Main Meals: 12 - 2.30 & 5 - 7.30 Mon - Sat, 12 - 4 Sun

Robinsons Hatters	H
Robinsons Best Bitter	H
Robinsons Hartleys XB	H

The Three Bears was opened in 1994 in a pleasant residential area on the southern edge of Hazel Grove, facing open fields across Jackson's Lane. It is the only pub for almost a mile in any direction and so not surprisingly, enjoys a healthy local trade, and is seldom less than busy. The pub is a compact, free-standing, brick building, which is basically one room, divided by partitions into three separate areas with plenty of comfortable seating. The extensive menu is very popular. The seating area nearest the food servery is a no-smoking area during the hours when food is available.
It is a rare regular local outlet for Hartleys XB (which enjoys a strong following in the pub) and has a Children's Certificate with children welcome

THREE TUNNES   H4
194 London Road, SK7 4DQ
Tel: 0161 483 3563
BR, Buses: 191, 192, 199
11.30 - 11 Mon - Sat, 12 - 10.30 Sun
Main Meals: 12 - 2 Mon - Fri

| Robinsons Hatters | H |
| Robinsons Best Bitter | H |

With its red brick and mock Tudor gabled exterior the "Tunnes" is one of Hazel Grove's oldest surviving pubs. The five rooms are plainly decorated with a minimalistic approach to artifacts on the walls, limited to a few brewery mirrors in two of the rooms. Customers span all generations and mix well in a friendly atmosphere, often with a constant scream of laughter from the vault. Noteworthy features are the old cast iron cooking range in the back lounge and the old fashioned sign of the "Three Tunnes" hanging outside. Easy to miss is the small beer garden across the car park to the rear. Lunches are of the no-nonsense burger/chips variety.

WHITE HART
259 London Road, SK7 4PL
opposite junction of Chester Road
12 - 11 Mon - Sat, 12 - 10.30 Sun

| Robinsons Hatters | E |
| Robinsons Best Bitter | E |

Small, welcoming, open-plan pub. Simply decorated and uncluttered.

WOODMAN
60 London Road, SK7 4AX
junction of Brewers Green
12 - 11 Mon - Sat, 12 - 10.30 Sun

| Robinsons Best Bitter | H |

Old pub with drastically altered interior and popular with young crowd. Pool and karaoke feature, with fancy dress events.

HEALD GREEN (SEE UNDER GATLEY & HEALD GREEN, PAGE 37)

THE HEATONS

HEATON CHAPEL, HEATON MOOR & HEATON NORRIS

ACKNOWLEDGEMENT

The pen and ink drawings of the Arden Arms; Crown, Heaton Lane; Swan With Two Necks and Railway are by Rosemary Wignall. Shown on this page are extracts from her limited edition pencil drawing prints of Heaton Moor Road which include The Crown (above) and The Plough (below). Rosemary also works in watercolour. Should anyone be interested in her work, she can be contacted on 0161 432 2509.

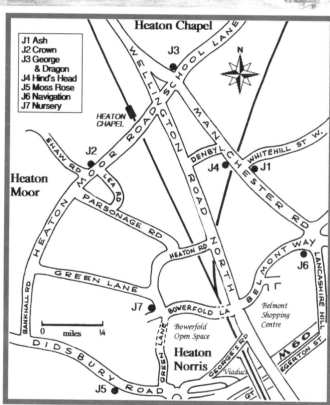

J1 Ash
J2 Crown
J3 George & Dragon
J4 Hind's Head
J5 Moss Rose
J6 Navigation
J7 Nursery

Heaton Chapel

Heaton Moor

Bowerfold Open Space

Belmont Shopping Centre

Heaton Norris

HEATON CHAPEL, HEATON MOOR & HEATON NORRIS

ASH   J1

232 Manchester Road, SK4 1NN
Tel: 0161 476 0399 Fax 0161 477 8604
junction of Whitehill Street West
Buses: 373 (or M/cr bound 192 to Wellington Rd.
N. jct. of Denby Lane. 1/3 mile walk)
12 - 11 Mon - Wed, 12 - 12 Thu - Sat, 12 - 10.30 Sun
Main Meals: 12 - 7 Sun - Fri, 12 - 9 Sat

Boddingtons Bitter	H
Guest Beer	H

The date on the ornate exterior proclaims the Ash to have been built in 1901 but there has been a pub on this site for hundreds of years. Following a major refurbishment, which has transformed the interior, customers have come back in their droves, following years of decline. A large open plan pub, very comfortably furnished, with a dining area housing the dart board in the evenings; vault area with pool and large screen TV for football, and a sizeable function room to the rear. There is entertainment every Thursday and Friday night. As well as being the home of the Reddish Blues (Manchester City), the pub has become very popular for food. The garden is one of the best in the area for children, with swings and slides and is a pleasant place for parents to have a drink while the kids play safely.

BLUE CAT
17 Shaw Road, SK4 4AG
NO REAL ALE

CHAPEL HOUSE
394a Wellington Road North, SK4 5AD
NO REAL ALE

CROWN   J2

98 Heaton Moor Road, SK4 4NZ
opposite Lea Road
BR (Heaton Chapel), Buses:, 22, 42A, 197
12 - 11 Mon - Sat, 12 - 10.30 Sun

Greenalls Bitter	H
Boddingtons Bitter	H

The Crown was formerly part of the estate of Clarke's Reddish Brewery, taken over by Boddingtons in 1964 and is now part of the Scottish Courage Group. It is a fine, multi-roomed local, boasting the only vault in Heaton Moor. The lounge areas comprise a small snug on the right as you enter the front door; a large and comfortably furnished lounge (with fire in winter) and a smaller rear lounge providing televised sport. The splendid traditional vault has its own entrance, from a passage on the right of the pub. Darts teams are based in the vault and crib and dominoes are regularly played here. An intended refurbishment may add to some facilities and hopefully will retain the character of the pub.

DILLONS WHISTLIN' JIG
19 Wellington Road North, SK4 1HJ
NO REAL ALE

ELIZABETHAN
33 Heaton Moor Road, SK4 4PB
NO REAL ALE

A beer is NOT just a beer. All told, there are 27 different styles of beer, with a further breakdown of 49 sub styles.

45

GEORGE AND DRAGON   J3

422 Manchester Road, SK4 5DH
Tel: 0161 431 7629
corner of School La, centre of Heaton Chapel
BR, Buses: 42A, 192, 373
11.30 - 11 Mon - Sat, 12 - 10.30 Sun
Main Meals: 12 - 7 Mon - Fri, 12 - 6 Sat, 12 - 5 Sun

Boddingtons Bitter	H
Occasional guest	H

A thriving community local at the centre of Heaton Chapel with an imposing brick and stone exterior which is common to a number of buildings in the area. This sizeable pub has a number of distinct areas, which ensure that even when the place is busy (with sport on the three television screens or entertainment) you can still normally find a quiet spot to have a conversation. The pub is well furnished and decorated with pictures of the local Stockport area. During the day, the lounge area becomes the dining room together with the raised "no smoking" area.

GRAPES

2 Quantock Close, SK4 1LF
turn right at end of Nicholson Street, off Lancashire Hill
11 - 11 Mon - Sat, 12 - 10.30 Sun

Boddingtons Bitter	H
Robinsons Best Bitter	H

Originally a parsonage, the Grapes was converted into a pub about 1820. A central bar serves a busy vault to the left and a lounge to the right which is divided into three distinct areas.

GREY HORSE

89 Old Road, SK4 1TE
at the top of Wharf Street, behind Nelstrop's Flour Mill
11 - 11 Mon - Sat, 12 - 10.30 Sun

Flowers IPA	H

This pub has a basic vault and large comfortable lounge which is divided into two areas. Stained glass screens are displayed above the bar in the lounge.

HIND'S HEAD   J4

Manchester Road, SK4 2RB
Tel: 0161 432 9301
corner of Denby Lane
Buses: 373 (or M/cr bound 192 to Wellington Rd. N. jct. of Denby Lane. 1/3 mile walk)
11.30 - 11 Mon - Sat, 12 - 10.30 Sun
Main Meals: 12 - 2 & 7 - 9 Mon - Sat, 12 - 3 Sun

Black Sheep Bitter	H
John Smiths Cask Bitter	H
Marstons Pedigree	H
Timothy Taylor Landlord	H
Morlands Old Speckled Hen	H
Guest Beer	H

The most upmarket pub in the area, the Hinds Head is an excellent example of a country style pub set in its own garden, in the suburbs. This comfortable single-roomed pub has a strong emphasis on good food, with the conservatory designated as the restaurant area. However the Hinds Head is also an attractive, friendly place to have a drink in a pleasant atmosphere. The pub has the widest range of beers in the

Heatons albeit at the high end of the price range. Once a month there is a pub quiz and themed food night.

HOPE INN
118 Wellington Road North, SK4 2LL
NO REAL ALE

LONSDALE
Belmont Way, SK4 1QX
NO REAL ALE

THE MOSS ROSE - SOON TO BE RENAMED?

MAGNET
51 Wellington Road North, SK4 1HJ
near junction of Georges Road
12.30 - 11 Mon - Sat, 10.30 - 11 Sun

John Smiths Bitter	H
Websters Bitter	H

The Magnet has a large lounge and smaller vault. Originally owned by the Royal Oak Brewery, Higher Hillgate.

MOOR TOP
172 Heaton Moor Road, SK4 4DU
NO REAL ALE

MOSS ROSE   J5
63 Didsbury Road, SK4 2BA
Tel: 0161 442 9510
opposite Crescent Park
Buses: 20, 23A, 42, 370
11.30 - 11 Mon - Sat, 12 - 10.30 Sun
Bar Snacks: Hot Bar Snacks 12 - 2 & 4 - 6pm

Hydes Light	H
Hydes Bitter	H

The Moss Rose was built in 1971 and from the exterior could be considered as a contender for Stockport's most unattractive pub. The inside has a traditional and homely feel, comprising a vault with numerous trophies and a large lounge. The impressive cellar facilities unusually include separate cellars for mild and bitter. The pub was due to undergo an extensive refit as this guide was printed, so details will vary. It is believed that the pub's name may also change.

According to a diary entry from a passenger on the Mayflower, the pilgrims made their landing at Plymouth Rock, rather than continue to their destination in Virginia, due to lack of beer.

NAVIGATION   J6

1 Manchester Road, SK4 1TY
Tel: 0161 480 6626
on roundabout at junction of Lancashire Hill
Buses: 203, 373, 375
12 - 11 Mon - Sat, 12 - 10.30 Sun
Bar Snacks: All Day

Beartown Bearskinful	**H**
Beartown Bruin's Ruin	**H**
Beartown Kodiak Gold	**H**
Beartown Polar Eclipse	**H**
Beartown Wheat Bear	**H**
Guest Cider	**H**

The Navigation takes its name from the canal (long ago filled in) which used to enable transport of materials to and from the nearby flour mill. The pub was originally owned by the Royal Oak Brewery, Higher Hillgate, later taken over by the Manchester Brewery Company, a subsidiary of Walker & Homfray of Salford. Situated on a busy roundabout parking is limited, although there are several quiet streets behind the pub. The Navigation comprises a long comfortably furnished lounge and a smaller vault, both served by a central bar. For years the Navigation did little trade until in December 2001, Beartown Brewery took the pub over and transformed its fortunes. After much hard work by the new licensee and her family, the Navigation is now thriving and the pub is an excellent example of how a combination of a new brewery making first class beer, and hard work, can turn a failing business around. Stockport and South Manchester CAMRA Pub of the Year 2003.

NICHOLSONS ARMS

2 Penny Lane, SK5 7RN
off Lancashire Hill
11 - 11 Mon - Sat, 12 - 10.30 Sun

Robinsons Hatters	**E**
Robinsons Best Bitter	**E**

Large lounge and vault with a central bar. There is also a small terrace outside. A bright and airy pub of modern design.

NURSERY   J7

258 Green Lane, SK4 2NA
Tel: 0161 432 2044
just off A6 by Dunham Jaguar (Heaton Road)
Buses: M/cr bound 192 to Wellington Rd. N. jct. of Belmont Way. Half-mile walk along Bowerfold La.
11.30 - 3 & 5.30 - 11 Mon - Fri, 11.30 - 11 Sat, 12 - 10.30 Sun
Main Meals: 12 - 2 Mon - Fri, 12 - 2.30 Sat - Sun

Hydes Mild	**E**
Hydes Bitter	**E**
Hydes Jekyll's Gold	**H**
Hydes Seasonal Guest	**H**

In 2001 the Nursery won CAMRA's National Pub of the Year title, having already gained similar awards from the local branch and the Greater Manchester Region. This is a very prestigious accolade only rarely given to pubs in urban areas, and had never before been won by a brewery-owned managed pub. But the Nursery is an exceptional pub, and its tucked-away location may have helped it preserve its character.

Although it is only half a mile from the busy A6 and Didsbury Road, and about a mile from Stockport town centre, the Nursery seems a world away, set in a quiet, leafy suburban area with little through traffic. It stands in a conservation area on a narrow cobbled street lined with

Victorian cottages. The site of Stockport County's original ground is very near here. The Nursery was built in 1939, replacing an earlier inn of the same name, and won a Civic Trust award at the time. It is an almost totally unspoilt example of the restrained, functional but high-quality design of the period. Externally it is perhaps a little square and square-cut, but inside is a warm, cosy multi-roomed interior. The windows feature a variety of subtle stained glass gardening motifs in line with the pub's name. There is a drinking corridor running through the pub from front to back, and three main rooms arranged around a central bar servery. There's a plain vault, which can only be reached from the other public areas by going outside, and a comfortable smoke room with a bow window looking out over the bowling green. A superb lounge runs along the front of the pub with full light oak panelling, bench seating and still retaining the bell-pushes for waiter service, although this facility is sadly no longer on offer. The consistency of the beer quality is reflected by the fact that in 2003 the Nursery celebrates its twentieth consecutive year in CAMRA's national Good Beer Guide, by some margin the longest continuous record in the area. Food is a major attraction, with a wide range of mostly home-made dishes on offer with set Sunday lunches which are especially highly regarded. The lounge is now used as a dining room at lunchtimes but reverts to normal pub function in the evenings. Children are welcome here if dining. Televised football is available in the vault with the pub having a strong Manchester City following, and the lounge sometimes hosts live music on Saturday nights. For its rare combination of unspoilt and lovingly-maintained 1930s pub design, and close attention to quality and detail in every aspect of service, this is a must-visit pub. The Nursery is a CAMRA National Inventory pub.

ORANGERY
54 Heaton Moor Road, SK4 4NZ
NO REAL ALE

PLOUGH
82 Heaton Moor Road, SK4 4NZ
opposite junction of Lea Road, in shopping parade
II - II Mon - Sat, I2 - I0.30 Sun

Tetley Bitter	H

A fine exterior of sandstone and Cheshire brick. The interior is a tasteful, multi-alcove arrangement with woodwork and stained glass. Comfortably furnished.

RAILWAY
74 - 76 Wellington Road North, SK4 IHF
opposite junction of Georges Road
I2 - II Mon - Sat, I2 - I0.30 Sun

Boddingtons Bitter	H
Theakstons Bitter	H

A large comfortably furnished pub comprised of three rooms served by a central bar.

RUDYARD
271 Wellington Road North, SK4 5BP
NO REAL ALE

SILVER JUBILEE
21 Hamilton Square, SK4 IJG
next to Belmont shopping centre, Belmont Way
II.30 - II Mon - Sat, I2 - I0.30 Sun

Robinsons Hatters	H
Robinsons Old Stockport	H
Robinsons Best Bitter	H

A simple layout, with a central bar serving a vault on one side and a large lounge with a tropical fish tank on the other. There is also a pleasant garden which is surrounded by a wall which affords some privacy.

THREE CROWNS
Manchester Road, SK4 ITN
NO REAL ALE

TOWN
60 Heaton Moor Road, SK4 4NZ
NO REAL ALE

> *I THINK THIS WOULD BE A GOOD TIME FOR A BEER."*
> *(UPON SIGNING THE NEW DEAL, PAVING THE WAY FOR THE REPEAL OF PROHIBITION)*

HEATON MERSEY

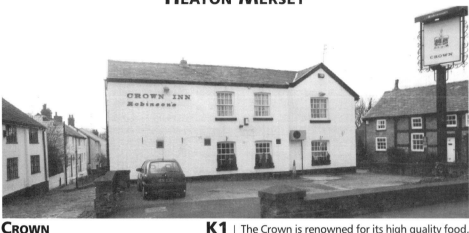

CROWN   K1
6 Vale Close, off Didsbury Road, SK4 3DS
Tel: 0161 442 4531
Buses: 20, 23A, 42, 42A, 370
11 - 11 Mon - Sat, 12 - 10.30 Sun
Main Meals: 12 - 2 Mon - Sat, 6.30 - 8.30 Tue - Fri,
12 - 3 Sun
   Robinsons Hatters   E
   Robinsons Best Bitter   E
Located at the top of a cobbled street (and conservation area), The Crown is one of the oldest pubs in Stockport (approx 400 years). This whitewashed building is entered via the side up some steps and through a patio (with tables for outdoor drinking). Upon entry there is an open pub with two characteristic areas - to the right is the older bar area and to the left is a modern lounge/dining area. There are many distinctive features including original wood beams, pew seating (both areas) and many brass plates hang off the walls.

The Crown is renowned for its high quality food, for which it has won many awards. The clientele normally consists of daytime diners and seasoned regulars/drinkers, whilst in the evening the Crown becomes a traditional drinking venue.

DOG AND PARTRIDGE
687 - 693 Didsbury Road, SK4 3AJ
opposite junction with Burnage Lane
11 - 11 Mon - Sat, 12 - 10.30 Sun
   Boddingtons Bitter   H
   Worthington Best Bitter   H
A basic conventional 1960's exterior houses a small lounge-like vault on one side and a larger open-plan bar on the other.

FROG AND RAILWAY
474 Didsbury Road, SK4 3BS
NO REAL ALE

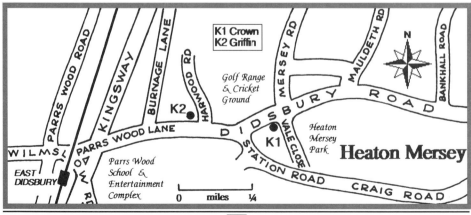

GRIFFIN K2

552 Didsbury Road, SK4 3AJ
Tel: 0161 443 2077
junction of Harwood Road
BR (East Didsbury), Buses:, 20, 23A, 42, 42A, 370
12 - 11 Mon - Sat, 12 - 10.30 Sun
Main Meals: 12 - 2 daily

Holt Mild	H
Holt Bitter	H
Holt Seasonal Beer	H

The Griffin is a friendly local multi-roomed pub, saved from demolition in the 1970s. It has two fine traditional bar gantrys in mahogany and etched glass. The main bar area with its large open plan room is in fact an extension to the pub, which could easily be mistaken as an original part. There is a protection order on the original main bar. The glass in the extension was relocated from the original shutters on the bar. There are several other original rooms, including a "news room" and a "smoke room" with pictures of old Heaton Mersey. Other notable features include a neat, spacious beer garden with an aviary full of budgerigars, etched glass front windows, and towards the back, many pictures of the pub. There are many Manchester City F.C. pictures including a magnificent oil painting of Neil Young's 1969 cup winning goal. The Griffin is a traditional pub with something for everyone including the cheapest beer in the area. A definite "must see" pub.

HEAVILEY

(SEE UNDER CALE GREEN, EDGELEY
AND HEAVILEY PAGE 18)

HIGH LANE

BULLS HEAD
28 Buxton Road, SK6 8BH
by Macclesfield Canal bridge
11 - 11 Mon - Sat, 12 - 10.30 Sun
   Boddingtons Bitter   H
Comfortable local by the Macclesfield Canal Bridge. Caters for most age-groups and tastes.

DOG AND PARTRIDGE
88 Buxton Road, SK6 8HJ
opposite Russell Avenue
11 - 11 Mon - Sat, 12 - 10.30 Sun
   Boddingtons Bitter   H
   Marstons Pedigree (occasional)   H
Large open-plan pub with accent on food. Has an indoor children's play area.

HORSESHOE   L1
1 Buxton Road, SK6 8AA
Tel: 01663 762487
junction with Windlehurst Road
Buses: 199
12 - 11 Mon - Sat, 12 - 10.30 Sun
Main Meals: 12 - 2.30 & 5.30 - 7.30 Tue - Sat, 12 - 6 Sun, no food Mon
   Robinsons Hatters   H
   Robinsons Best Bitter   H
Set on a corner of the road that takes you to Hawk Green, this is a comfortable semi-open pub with a separate non-smoking dining room and darts area to the right. The pub has been

on the site since around 1800, originally serving coal miners from the long since disused local pits. Nowadays, it is a pleasant pub with a friendly approach and a reputation for good value food. Although the decor is somewhat muted, there are some interesting old photographs of bygone High Lane, a Titanic feature, a pot shire horse collection and some tasteful painted renderings of the pub building. Note the gigantic horseshoe over the front door as you enter, it seems to form part of the inn sign.

RED LION
112 Buxton Road, SK6 8ED
opposite Andrew Lane
11.30 - 11 Mon - Sat, 12 - 10.30 Sun
   Robinsons Hatters   E
   Robinsons Best Bitter   E
Large well-appointed roadhouse with the emphasis on food. Accommodation is available.

ROBIN HOOD
Buxton Road, SK7 6NA
near junction of Wellington Road
12 - 11 Mon - Sat, 12 - 10.30 Sun
   Robinsons Hatters   E
   Robinsons Best Bitter   E
Large pub on busy A6 main road. Beer garden, functions catered for and live entertainment at weekends. Food available.

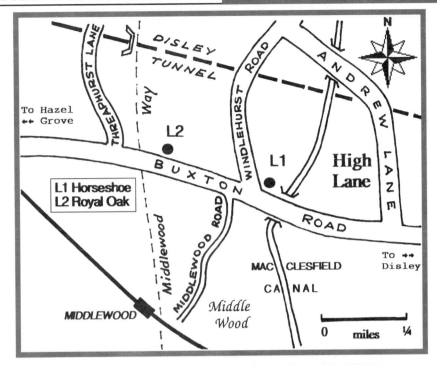

ROYAL OAK L2

Buxton Road, SK6 8AY
Tel: 01663 762380
east of Threaphurst Lane, near
Middlewood Way
Buses: 199
12 - 3 & 6 - 11 Mon - Sat (11 - 11 in summer), 12 - 10.30 Sun
Main Meals: 6 - 8 Tue - Fri, 12 - 8 Sat - Sun,
no food Mon

Burtonwood Bitter	**H**
Two Guest Beers	**H**

On this site since 1800, the pub is a large, whitewashed building with its own cobbled forecourt, laid out with picnic tables (not to mention a planter in the form of an old bath). The interior is opened out to an extent, but retains a country pub feel with plush rustic decor and lots of brass, copperware, hunting horns, model shire horses and so on. Of particular note are the two splendid overmantles, cleverly used to form the bar back - one is mirrored, Gothic in style, whilst the other seems Victorian. There is a large lounge to the left, a snug-cum-TV room to the front right and a pool room with pinball machine to the rear right. At the back lies a tidily kept, enclosed garden with a pond and dovecote.

A basketball hoop has also been provided at the very rear car park for those more athletically inclined. Entertainment appears every Friday and a weekly quiz is held on Tuesdays.

> *FERMENTATION MAY HAVE BEEN A*
> *GREATER DISCOVERY THAN FIRE*
> *- DAVID RAINS WALLACE*

"DRINK HARD CIDER AS MUCH AS YER PLEASE"

BY JOHN REEK

'Drink hard cider as much as yer please
Lose yer teeth and bow yer knees
Sours yer gut and makes yer wheeze
Turns yer words to sting o'bees
Thins yer blood and kills yer fleas
Drink hard cider as much as yer please.' (Origin Somerset)

Hopefully the cider we get in Stockport isn't quite as vicious these days!

THE term 'hard' refers to cider that has problems such as oxidisation, acetification, mouse, etc. Prior to Pasteur's discoveries, which led to a clearer understanding of what happens during fermentation and subsequent maturation, lots of cider would probably have been like this.

A Research Centre was set up at Long Ashton, near Bristol, in the early part of the last century to study cider apples, and how the diversity of taste, colour and character could be developed. Amongst other activities, they planted cider apple trees, perry pear trees, made single variety ciders, and held competitions, which proved to be very important in the development of modern cidermaking techniques. I somehow can't imagine getting the Monday morning blues if working at such a place! Sadly, Long Ashton is now closed and the workers, some of whom had been there for decades, have been retired. Many were given cider jugs and commemorative bottles, dating from Long Ashton's inception to its demise in 2003. The apple and pear trees are in the process of being rooted up and people will be living where this place once provided employment for locals.

There are four categories when classifying cider flavour components - sweet, bitter-sweet, sharp and bitter-sharp. These terms refer to the relative proportions of sugar (sweet), acid (sharp) and tannin (bitter) in the fruit. For example, the famous Kingston Black apple is a bitter-sharp variety, while Yarlington Mill is bitter-sweet. It is mainly the tannin element that distinguishes a cider apple from the cookers and eaters, such that cider made from cooking apples is sharp and sweet, lacking the astringency and length of flavour that the tannin brings. In my opinion, both styles have their merits which attract their respective aficionados.

Back to Stockport! Not being historically a cider-producing nor-cider drinking area, the earliest knowledge I have of cider for sale in our venerable hostelries dates back to around the mid 1960s. The Griffin, on Didsbury Road, used to sell cider at a cost of 6d (2 ½ p) when the ale was 7d (3p). I am reliably informed that the cider wasn't that pleasant, perhaps similar to the type of brew mentioned at the beginning of this article.

Stockport Beer Festival has always had an extensive cider bar, and it was here that I was introduced to cider made by artisans. I had always drunk beer up to this point but after trying this type of craft-made cider, I was converted. Unfortunately, I can't recall the original make of cider but it reminded me of liquid Christmas pudding. Stockport Beer Festival's cider bar has continued to grow, thanks to the pioneering efforts of those early enthusiasts.

It almost goes without saying that the best pubs in which to drink cider and perry are those that offer a choice from smaller, independent producers as opposed to the mediocre mass-produced concoctions that the big boys want to foist on the less well-informed drinking public. One of the earliest pioneering pubs in this area that sold real cider was the Crown, on Heaton Lane, where alongside the fine cask beers on offer, a traditional cider was introduced by the then licensee Ken Birch. A couple of years later, Dave Porter opened up the Railway, in Portwood and immediately offered real cider, aided by an ingenious cooling system that maintained the cider at an ideal drinking temperature. Unusually, around this time, Stockport had the luxury of being served by four full-time and one occasional cider agents. Not long after this, Steve Brannan took over the Olde Vic, Edgeley and introduced a regular real cider, plus the occasional guests. More recently, Angie and Chantal at the Navigation, Lancashire Hill, have transformed this erstwhile run-down pub into a welcoming local with an enterprising range of at least three ciders or perries.

All in all, a very healthy local situation for those who enjoy genuine traditional cider, as opposed to the nasty hard variety mentioned in the title!

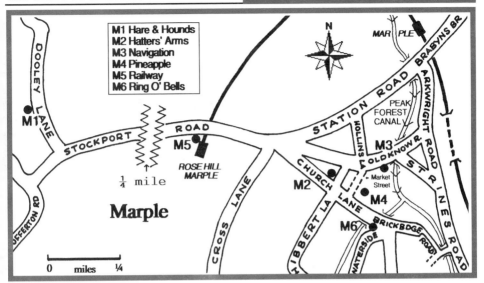

M1 Hare & Hounds
M2 Hatters' Arms
M3 Navigation
M4 Pineapple
M5 Railway
M6 Ring O' Bells

¼ mile

ROSE HILL
MARPLE

Marple

0   miles   ¼

MARPLE

BULLS HEAD
23 Market Street, SK6 7AA
11 - 11 Mon - Sat, 12 - 10.30 Sun
Robinsons Hatters   H
Robinsons Best Bitter   H
Ideally situated in the centre of Marple. It remains a basic, beer-drinking boozer.

CROWN
1 Hawk Green Road, Hawk Green, SK6 7HU
junction of Upper Hibbert Lane
11 - 11 Mon - Sat, 12 - 10.30 Sun
Robinsons Hatters   H
Robinsons Best Bitter   H
Robinsons Seasonal Guest   H
Long, low, mock-Tudor house fronting the large
village green. Recently heavily refurbished along
the lines of the 'upmarket boozer-cum-restaurant'
theme. Topers, TV sports watchers and diners
happily co-exist in a modern-meets-tradition atmosphere. Food served every day 12 till 9.

HARE & HOUNDS   M1
Dooley Lane, SK6 7EJ
Tel: 0161 427 0293
**Buses: 358, 383 (384 return) alight Marple Road
/ Dooley Lane - third of a mile walk**
12 - 11 Mon - Sat, 12 - 10.30 Sun
*Main Meals: 12 - 2 & 6 - 8 Mon - Fri, 12 - 9 Sat, 12
- 6.30 Sun*
Hydes Bitter   H
Hydes Seasonal Guest   H

Dating from the 1780s, the pub lies on a now
by-passed section of road close by historic
Chadkirk Chapel and the sharply angled
Otterspool Bridge. It became a Showells of
Hempshaw Lane pub in the 1880s, most recently it fell into the ownership of Hydes in late
2002. This had the effect of bringing Hydes
beers to the village for the first time. Styled as
one of their 'Heritage Inns', it offers steaks and
such in a family dining atmosphere. The building is in two parts - the older half holds the bar
and its panelled, low-beamed surroundings. The
newer half is also beamed, but is now a dining
area, with conservatory off. The beer garden
fronts the new cut of Dooley Lane.

HATTERS ARMS M2

81 Church Lane, SK6 7AW
Tel: 0161 427 1529
junction of Hibbert Lane
Buses: 358, 383, 384
12 - 11 Mon - Sat, 12 - 10.30 Sun
Main Meals: 12 - 2 Mon - Sun, 6 - 9 Mon - Sat

Robinsons Hatters	H
Robinsons Best Bitter	H
Robinsons Seasonal Guest	H

This has always been a little gem. On the end of a row of stone-built hatters' cottages - hence the name. There has been some modernisation which fortunately is not as drastic as some of Robinson's more brutal, earlier efforts. The panelling in the bar is intact and the small rooms make for a snug and cosy feel. After years of defiant traditionalism under formidable landlady Sadie, the present couple have introduced very good catering. Original bell pushes restored to full working order - service can be at table.

NAVIGATION M3

9 Stockport Road, SK6 6BD
Tel: 0161 427 2270
junction of Lockside
Buses: 358, 383, 384
11.30 - 11 Mon - Sat, 12 - 10.30 Sun
Main Meals: 12 - 2 Tues - Sat

Robinsons Hatters	H
Robinsons Best Bitter	H
Robinsons Seasonal Guest	H

Named for its proximity to the Peak Forest Canal and the spectacular series of Marple locks, the Navigation was also famous as the place where all Marple buses stopped. In competition with all the other Robinsons pubs in this virtual monopoly area, it was opened out some time ago but still retains a rather comfortable little vault at the front of the pub. There is catering during the day, but concentration on beer at night.

MARPLE'S "GRAND AQUEDUCT"

BY MARK MCCONACHIE

Local industrialist Samuel Oldknow of Mellor was instrumental in the construction of the Peak Forest Canal, which runs from Whaley Bridge in Derbyshire to Dukinfield in Cheshire. At Marple, just beyond bottom lock, it crosses the River Goyt on a magnificent three arched, pierced, stone aqueduct. This was constructed and designed by Benjamin Outram (who went on to invent the tram car), in 1794. It took seven years to build and seven men were killed during its construction. At the time it was known as the "Grand Aqueduct", being 100 feet above the river and 309 feet in length. It was said that people came from all over the country to view this remarkable construction. The aqueduct is now a Grade II* listed structure and is commemorated by a blue Millennium plaque.

OTTERS LODGE
Cross Lane, SK6 7PZ
NO REAL ALE

PINEAPPLE M4
45 Market Street, SK6 7AA
Tel: 0161 427 3935
near junction of Church Lane
Buses: 358, 383, 384
11 - 11 Mon - Sat, 12 - 10.30 Sun
Robinsons Hatters H
Robinsons Best Bitter H
Robinsons Seasonal Guest (occasional) H
At the top end of Marple's little precinct, the Pineapple is resolutely non-food and proud of

it. This is an attractive brick pub: inside there is a lot of scope for activity. To the right there is a comfortable bar-lounge with an open fire in winter; to the left is a large vault with plenty of room for cards and darts. There is a large pool room and next door an attractive little meeting room used for small private functions and the quiz team.

RAILWAY M5
223 Stockport Road, SK6 6EN
Tel: 0161 427 2146
by Rose Hill station
BR (Rose Hill from Mcr.), Buses:, 358, 383 (384 return)
11.45 - 11 Mon - Sat. 12 - 10.30 Sun
Main Meals: 12 - 2 Daily
Robinsons Hatters H
Robinsons Best Bitter H
Robinsons Seasonal Guest (occasional) H
With an impressive facade, this pub opened in 1878 alongside Rose Hill station - whose Manchester commuters it still serves. Replacing a former beer house (Gun Inn), the pub was originally owned by Bells Brewery and is little changed externally, although is typical Robinson's modern house style inside. Handy for walkers and cyclists on the nearby Middlewood Way, its two pleasant open plan rooms have an airy relaxing atmosphere. The landlord recently won Robinsons best kept cellar competition. Children welcome up to 3.00pm.

> *On October 17 of 1814, a rupture in a brewery tank containing 3,500 barrels of beer caused a flood of fatal proportions in the London parish of St. Giles. The wave of beer swept victims off their feet, dashed them against walls, and buried them under debris. Two houses were demolished in the sea of beer suddenly loosed upon town, and nine people lost their lives in the flood of suds.*

RING O' BELLS M6

130 Church Lane, SK6 7AY
Tel: 0161 427 2300
by Bridge 2 of Macclesfield Canal
Buses: 358, 383, 384
11.30 - 3 & 5.30 - 11 Mon - Fri, 11.30 - 11 Sat, 12 - 10.30 Sun
Main Meals: 11.30 - 2.00 & 5.30 - 8.30 Tues - Sat, 12 - 7 Sun

Robinsons Hatters	H
Robinsons Best Bitter	H
Robinsons Seasonal Guest	H

Attractively situated above the town centre next to the Macclesfield Canal, commanding extensive views over the surrounding hills. Retains two cosy snugs at the front, with a more open-plan layout around the bar counter and towards the rear. There is a pleasant beer garden alongside the canal and the pub is deservedly popular for its excellent food, served lunchtimes and evenings, but also has a strong regular patronage from its active teams in local quiz and crib leagues. Robinsons Bar & Cellar Competition 2002 overall champion.

MARPLE BRIDGE

(SEE UNDER COMPSTALL & MARPLE BRIDGE PAGE 34)

MARPLE RIDGE

ROMPER INN
Ridge End, SK6 7ET
junction of Hollinwood Lane
12 - 3 & 6 - 11 Mon - Sat, 12 - 10.30 Sun

| Boddingtons Bitter | H |
| Three Guest Beers | H |

Four rambling, linked rooms all on differing levels. Plenty of exposed stone and good 'country carpenter' oak fittings in what is predominantly a food house. Prices can be on the high side but are offset by the pub's stunning setting.

MELLOR

DEVONSHIRE ARMS
307 Longhurst Lane, SK6 5PP
two miles out of Marple Bridge, junction of Moor End Road
12 - 3 & 5.30 - 11 Mon - Sat, 12 - 10.30 Sun

Robinsons Hatters	H
Robinsons Best Bitter	H
Robinsons Seasonal Guest	H

Lovely old pub with various well-furnished rooms. Good quality home-cooked food and pleasant outdoor dining area.

MOORFIELD
Shiloh Road, SK6 5NE
two-thirds of a mile north, off Moor End Road
12 - 2.30 & 6.30 - 11 Mon - Fri, 12 - 3 & 6.30 - 11 Sat, 12 - 3 & 6.30 - 10.30 Sun

| Marstons Pedigree | H |

Large pub/restaurant in pleasant countryside. Beer Garden. Function room available.

ODDFELLOWS ARMS N1
73 Moor End Road, SK6 5PJ
Tel: 0161 449 7826
2 1/2 miles east of Marple Bridge, near junction of Podnor Lane
Buses: 363 (limited Mo-Sa daytime service only)
11 - 3 & 5.30 - 11 Tues - Sat, 12 - 3 & 7 - 10.30 Sun, closed Mon
Main Meals: 12 - 2.30 & 6.30 - 9.30 Tue - Sat, 12 - 2 Sun

Adnams Bitter	H
Marstons Bitter	H
Marstons Pedigree	H
Guest Beer	H

The creeper-clad exterior of this stone-built, three storey building blends in so well with its surroundings that it can easily be missed, especially at night. Does this truly encompass that 'Roses around the door' ideal of a country pub? Well, yes it does. Firstly, it has a good range of

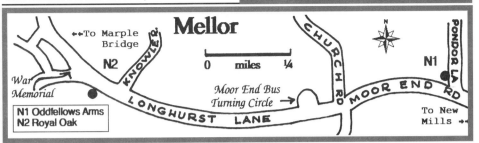

cask beers backed up by Cask Marque accreditation. Follow this with a number of beamed, low-ceilinged cosy rooms with coal fires, stone-flagged floors, settles and other assorted rustic furniture. Throw in brasses a-plenty and a china-laden dresser that add to the bucolic charm. Then finish off with a top-notch kitchen serving quality fare to both the bar and the upstairs restaurant, and you have yourself a pub that is well worth the excursion to its rural location.

ROYAL OAK N2
Longhurst Lane, SK6 5PT
Tel: 0161 427 1655
junction of Parkside Lane
Buses: 363 (limited Mo-Sa daytime service only)
5.30 - 11 Mon - Fri, 12 - 11 Sat, 12 - 10.30 Sun
5.30 - 10.30 Indian Restaurant (Daily)

Robinsons Hatters	H
Robinsons Best Bitter	H
Robinsons Seasonal Guest	H

This rendered, cottage-style pub in the centre of a terraced row was established in 1828 as a tavern and public house on the back New Mills road. Subtly altered of late to give a larger lounge area showing off its flagged floor and open-beamed ceiling bedecked with tankards, the walls also feature local artists' watercolour work. The right hand section contains an Indian restaurant (and takeaway) with quite an extensive menu on offer. Scenic views are afforded from the large, well tended beer garden at the rear. An unusual sport that plays a large part in the social life of the pub, and village for that matter, is Lacrosse.

OFFERTON

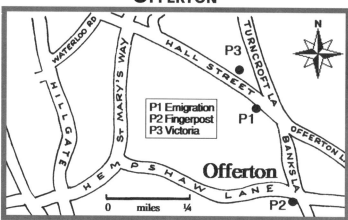

P1 Emigration
P2 Fingerpost
P3 Victoria

Offerton

0   miles   ¼

EMIGRATION   P1
166 Hall Street, SKI 4JG
Tel: 0161 477 8651
Buses: 314
11.30 - 11 Mon - Sat, 12 - 10.30 Sun
  Robinsons Hatters   H
  Robinsons Best Bitter   H
  Robinsons Seasonal Guest   H
The pub consists of three drinking areas, two at the front of the pub and a lounge to the rear. The front areas contain interesting old photos of Offerton. The rear lounge has recently been tastefully refurbished. Strong Darts, Crib and Football teams (The Stockport Nomads). Popular Quiz nights on Mondays. Pub caters for locals but all are made welcome in a pleasant drinking atmosphere. The pub name is believed to be the only one in the U.K. (some say named after a racehorse).

FINGERPOST   P2
434 Hempshaw Lane, SKI 4QA
Tel: 0161 480 4138
junction of Dialstone Lane
Buses: 358, 383 (384 return)
11 - 11 Mon - Sat, 12 - 10.30 Sun
  Robinsons Hatters   E
  Robinsons Best Bitter   E
This is a large corner pub located at a prominent crossroads. Built before the Great War, it has unusually retained six separate drinking areas. The bar is to the left of the entrance, with the lounge on the right housing a collection of pub mirrors and brass plates (note the 'Grunhalle clock' over mantelpiece!). The extremely spacious vault features photos of football teams and there is sports memorabilia throughout the pub. A meeting place for many social, political and sports clubs, the pub is also the headquarters of the Stockport County Independent Supporters Club.

GARDENERS ARMS
Little Street, SK2 5AB
junction of Banks Lane, Hall Street and Marple Road
12 - 11 Mon - Sat, 12 - 10.30 Sun
Boddingtons Bitter   H
Basically two large rooms separated by a large bar. TV, pool and dartboard in vault.

GOLDEN HIND
Lisburne Lane, SK2 5RH
NO REAL ALE

HARVESTER
23 Turnstone Road, SK2 5XT
off Marple Road, then Bean Leach Road then Shearwater Road
2 - 11 Mon - Thu, 11 - 11 Fri - Sat, 12 - 10.30 Sun
Greenalls Bitter   H
Marstons Pedigree   H
Greenalls Mild   H
Cosy ex -Greenalls pub. Lounge, vault, no-smoking, eating areas and small function room. The wooden ceiling is a nice feature as are the photos and fish tank on the bar.

PUSS IN BOOTS
147 Nangreave Road, SK2 6DG
opposite shopping parade
12 - 3 & 5 - 11 Mon - Fri, 12 - 11 Sat, 12 - 10.30 Sun
Robinsons Best Bitter   H
Uninspiring exterior fronts a genuine local. The non-standard Robbies interior is due to the previous tenure of Greenalls. Caters for functions and funeral parties.

STRAWBERRY GARDENS
84 Offerton Lane, SK2 5BS
NO REAL ALE

> *MANY PEOPLE TELL ME THEY HAVE VISITED THE US, FAILED TO FIND ANYTHING DRINKABLE AND TURNED IN DESPERATION TO IMPORTED BASS AND GUINNESS.*
>
> *THEY ARE UNAWARE THAT SOME 400 (NOW NEARLY 1,500) MICRO, CRAFT, NEW WAVE OR "SPECIALTY" BREWERS NOW OPERATE, MANY OF THEM CONCENTRATING ON ALES OF REMARKABLE QUALITY.*
>
> *SOURCE: ROGER PROTZ*

VICTORIA   P3
125 Hall Street, SK1 4HE
Tel: 0161 480 3983
Buses: 314
11.30 - 11 Mon - Sat, 12 - 10.30 Sun
Main Meals: 12 - 2.30 Mon - Sat
Cains Mild   H
Greenalls Bitter   H
Marstons Pedigree   H
Gust Beer   H
This white painted terraced property dating from 1840 sits snugly juxtaposed with other aged properties and the two sixties tower blocks on the village's main thoroughfare. Consisting of large, two roomed vault with a definite bent towards sport, darts, crib and table football all in evidence. The slightly smaller lounge is also well patronised and is decorated in a tastefully restrained manner with local artists' prints (for sale) and ceramic wall plates depicting WWII aircraft.

WHITE HOUSE
384 Hempshaw Lane, SK1 4NT
200 yards west of junction with Dialstone La.
5 - 11 Mon - Thu, 3-11 Fri, 12 - 11 Sat, 12 - 10.30 Sun
Boddingtons Bitter   H
Large pub with two lounges and vault. Tastefully refurbished with pictures of New York in the lounge.

WRIGHTS ARMS
198 Marple Road, SK2 5EU
junction of Bean Leach Road
12 - 11 Mon - Sat, 12 - 10.30 Sun
Flowers IPA   H
Two Guest Beers   H
Low ceilinged, and dating from the 1800s, it retains an air of rusticity. Two large rooms plus rear non smoking area.

PORTWOOD

MIDWAY TAVERN
263 Newbridge Lane, SK1 2NX
near junction of West Park Road
11 - 11 Mon - Sat, 12 - 10.30 Sun

Websters Green Label	H
Boddingtons Bitter	H
Guest Beer	H

Largish dining pub in a quiet part of town overlooking the River Goyt. Comprises lounge and separate restaurant . All tastefully done in plush-rustic.

OLD KING
60 Great Portwood Street, SK1 2HH
junction of Lancaster Street
11 - 11 Mon - Sat, 12 - 10.30 Sun

Robinsons Best Bitter	H

A large lounge with stage area and two table Pool room with a fabulous brown-glazed fireplace. To the left is a spacious long vault.

> *IT'S THE SAME THE WORLD OVER.*
> *ANYONE WHO HAS EVER WALKED UPRIGHT*
> *HAS LOVED BEER, CELEBRATED OVER IT,*
> *TOLD TALES OVER IT,*
> *HATCHED PLOTS OVER IT,*
> *COURTED OVER IT.*
> *IT'S WHAT WE DO AS A SPECIES.*
> *IT'S WHAT MAKES US HUMAN.*
> *WE BREW*
> *- ALAN "THE BEER KING" EAMES*

PARK   Q1
264 Newbridge Lane, SK1 2PG
Tel: 0161 480 2275
by junction of Carrington Road and New Zealand Road (B6104)
Buses: 330, 384 (383 return), 386
11.30 - 11 Mon - Sat, 12 - 10.30 Sun
Main Meals: 11.30 - 2.30 Mon - Fri, 12 - 5 Sat - Sun

Holt Bitter	H
Boddingtons Bitter	H

Situated by a busy crossroads, the Park takes its name from the nearby Vernon Park, which has been recently restored and is well worth a visit, Inside the layout is simple enough, a central bar serving a vault and a large lounge. The Park is very much a locals' pub which makes for a lively atmosphere. It has an eventful history and when opened in 1834, was known as the Hare and Hounds, being renamed the Park Hotel in 1858. Jonathan Needham brewed there in the 1860's but by 1880 the hotel was owned by Walker & Homfrays Brewery, which was in turn taken over by Wilsons.

QUEENS
11 Great Portwood Street, SK1 2DW
100 yards from junction of Knightsbridge
11 - 11 Mon - Sat, 12 - 10.30 Sun

Robinsons Hatters	E
Robinsons Best Bitter	E

A single room house with bar along the back wall. Large number of monochromed photos of old Stockport.

RAILWAY   Q2

1 Avenue Street, SK1 2BZ
Tel: 0161 429 6062
opposite Peel (shopping) Centre
Buses: 324, 325, 330
12 - 11 Mon - Sat, 12 - 10.30 Sun
Main Meals: 12 - 3 Mon - Sat

Porter Mild	H
Porter Bitter	H
Porter Floral Dance	H
Porter Rossendale	H
Porter Railway Sleeper	H
Porter Porter	H
Porter Sunshine	H
Porter Seasonal Guest	H
Guest Beer	H

Saved from dereliction by the Porter Brewing Co., the Railway is a 'must' when visiting Stockport.

Not much to look at from the outside, the interior comprises an 'L' shaped bar serving a large lounge. The welcome, however, is warm and the conversation engaging. From the energetic and enthusiastic licensee to the friendly and helpful bar staff, it's the people that make the Railway what it is. Add keenly priced beer and food, the latter home-cooked, and a range of foreign beers to rival any bar in the region, it's no wonder that the Railway has won a host of awards. Guest beer weekends are a highlight, guests change every week and always feature an independent brewery. Occasional Porter brew such as Stout, Ginger Tom, Celebration, Christmas Special. Real cider dispensed from tub on bar. Runner-up in CAMRA's National Pub of the Year competition for 2002.

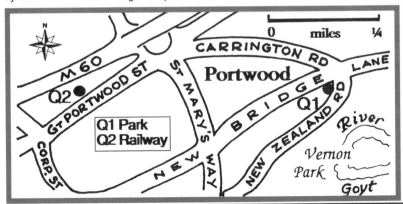

ROBINSON'S INVADES EUROPE
BY KAREN WAINWRIGHT

MANY of us have sampled foreign beers in bottles or draught in Britain but how many have been able to track down their favourite local tipple whilst abroad? Well, all that could be about to change as Robinson's are now exporting their beers to Italy and the United States.

The Rimini Trade Fair is the largest drinks show in Italy and six British brewers were invited to attend, being given a time slot of two months to supply 40 Italian bars. Amongst these brewers was Robinson's, who used the event last October to introduce cask-conditioned Frederic's. At the trade fair, attracting 150,000 visitors, the more discerning of Mediterranean Ale-imbibers consumed 16 firkins (9-gallon casks) of Frederic's, and 40 cases of Northern Glory! Buyers and beer writers were also able to attend workshops where they could taste Robinson's beers and learn more about them. The latest deal for the Italian market is for the supply of 300 firkins of Frederic's to be followed next season by bottled Old Tom. All too often, the only British beer available abroad is over-priced, over-gassed, under-flavoured mass market pap from the multi-national mega-keggery fizz factories that are gradually obtaining a stranglehold on British beer production. So, it is extremely encouraging that the Italians at least are getting an opportunity to try some quality British cask beer from one of out top regional and still family-owned traditional

breweries. If all goes to plan, Frederic's could be available in over one hundred bars in Italy in the not too distant future.

Robinson's have also been making inroads into the United States bottled beer market. However, with the huge recent rapid increase in the number of local American micro breweries, they face stiff competition in this small but growing area of a domestic market that is suffocated by a very few enormous international operators headed by Anheuser-Busch the perpetrators of American Budweiser. Undaunted, Robinson's are pressing ahead over the next twelve months with the shipment of 3000 cases of bottled Northern Glory, Double Hop and Old Tom, which are being distributed through the Capital Brewing Company based in Middleton, Wisconsin. These will be sold initially in bars, liquor stores and supermarkets in the states of Iowa, Illinois, Minnesota, Missouri, Ohio and Wisconsin.

Lets hope that the exportation of our better quality beers continues and that other like-minded cask breweries also consider exporting their beers to foreign climes in need of an infusion of tasty British ales.

REDDISH VALE VIADUCT
BY MARK McCONACHIE

This crosses the River Tame and bridges the gap between Brinnington and Reddish North stations on the Manchester to Marple and New Mills service. Constructed in brick, it opened in 1875 and consists of an impressive 13 arches. As well as serving rail passengers, it provides a fitting backdrop to the picturesque nature haven of Reddish Vale Country Park - home to a plethora of waterfowl. A true idyll for the weary folk of the north east of the borough

Floor mosaic at the entrance to the Tiviot, Stockport Town Centre

REDDISH

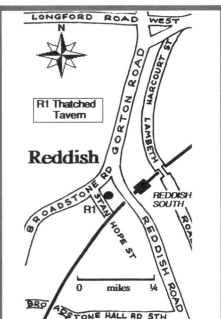

RAILWAY
465 Gorton Road, SK5 6LR
NO REAL ALE

REDDISH VALE
Longford Road West, SK5 6HX
NO REAL ALE

THATCHED TAVERN R1
54 Stanhope Street, SK5 7AQ
Tel: 0161 285 1830
off Houldsworth Square
Buses: 42A, 203, 373, 375
11.30 - 11 Mon - Sat, 12 - 10.30 Sun

Tetley Dark Mild	H
Tetley Bitter	H
Boddingtons Bitter	H

An archetypal street corner local, the like of which is becoming increasingly rare in the Stockport area. The Thatched Tavern is hidden away from traffic, avoiding the main roads through Reddish. If you persevere in finding the pub, you will be welcomed by the brightly lit exterior, fronting a comfortable lounge with a large picture of the original Thatched Tavern in 1882. The the pub really was thatched and was across the road from its current site, in a more rural setting than present day urban Reddish. The vault is split in two with the dart board in one area and crib tables, built by the licensee, in the other.

BULLS HEAD
605 Gorton Road, SK5 6NX
NO REAL ALE

CAROUSEL
156 Reddish Road, SK5 7HR
NO REAL ALE

FIR TREE
257 Gorton Road, SK5 6LL
junction of Longford Road West
12 - 11 Mon - Sat, 12 - 10.30 Sun

Tetley Bitter	H

A large roadhouse-type pub. The 'lounge' has TV, electronic games and four pool tables. The only pub in North Reddish to sell cask beer.

GREY HORSE
99 Broadstone Road, SK5 7AS
opposite Broadstone Mill
11.30 - 11 Mon - Sat, 12 - 10.30 Sun

Boddingtons Bitter	H

A sizeable pub with a brick and stone exterior, rebuilt 100 years ago. A large vault and extensive lounge.

HOULDSWORTH ARMS
1 Houldsworth Square, SK5 7AF
NO REAL ALE

UNION
93 Broadstone Road, SK5 7AS
opposite Broadstone Mill
11 - 11 Mon - Sat, 12 - 10.30 Sun

Robinsons Best Bitter	H

An open plan pub, pleasant and comfortable. The only independent brewers' owned pub in the Reddish area.

ROMILEY

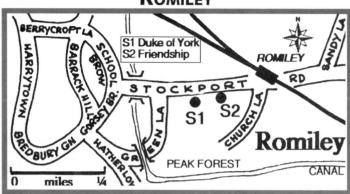

S1 Duke of York
S2 Friendship

ROMILEY

S1 S2

Romiley

PEAK FOREST

CANAL

0 miles ¼

CHERRY TREE
2 Compstall Road, SK6 4EW
NO REAL ALE

COW & CALF INN
School Brow, SK6 3AT
junction of Barrack Hill
II - II Mon - Sat, I2 - I0.30 Sun

Robinsons Hatters	E
Robinsons Best Bitter	E

Open-plan pub with separate dining room. Live entertainment at weekends.

DUKE OF YORK   S1
Stockport Road, SK6 3AN
Tel: 0161 430 2806
near junction of Green Lane
BR (from M/cr), Buses:, 384 (383 return), 386
I2 - II Mon - Sat. I2 - I0.30 Sun
Main Meals: All Day

Boddingtons Bitter	H
John Smiths Cask Bitter	H
Courage Directors	H
Draught Bass	H

A long, low pub of harmonious proportions that lies close to the popular Peak Forest Canal. Formerly a Yates' Brewery house, this is one of the village's oldest public houses - note the wagon arch at the

left hand side leading to the back of the property. Inside is a pleasing sense of tradition with a real fire, beamed ceiling and images of the pub in olden times in the front lounge. A raised, panelled lounge reached via some steps, lies off to the left of the entrance and provides a more intimate atmosphere for the quiet-minded toper. From the bar area, a door leads into a large cleanly decorated public bar with another smaller room (with its own fire) that caters for darts and crib. All in all, a pub that is well patronised and often bustling, where all types of clientele can surely find comfort within its walls.

FORRESTERS ARMS
29 Greave, SK6 4PU
near junction of Greave Fold
I2 - 3.30 & 5.30 - II Mon - Thu, I2 - II Fri - Sat, I2 - I0.30 Sun

Boddingtons Bitter	H

Popular pub with the local name 'Piggy'. Open-plan, comfortable and serving food in separate restaurant area.

FRIENDSHIP   S2
77 Stockport Road, SK6 3AA
Tel: 0161 494 2183
BR (from M/cr), Buses:, 384 (383 return), 386
II - II Mon - Sat, I2 - I0.30 Sun

Robinsons Hatters	H
Robinsons Best Bitter	H
Robinsons Seasonal Guest	H

Rendered and half-timbered roadside house that offers a cosy welcome through its arched porch. Formerly a Bells pub, it passed into the Robinsons estate in1949. Formal lounge to the left set out with discrete tables (with candles) and chairs instead of fixed seating. Across the corridor, to the side of the bar, are two small rooms, somewhat uncomfortably divided by the remnants of a chimney breast. A few pictures of old Stockport scenes

add to the decor. To the rear left is a quite commodious pool and darts room with all-round bench seating. A beer garden and children's play area lie to the rear, and beyond the car park, a splendidly maintained bowling green which is open for all to use. Jazz is played every Thursday and many sports teams make the pub their base.

GREY HORSE
51 Stockport Road, SK6 3AA
NO REAL ALE

RAILWAY
6 Stockport Road, SK6 4BN
by Romiley BR
12 - 11 Mon - Sat, 12 - 10.30 Sun

Robinsons Hatters	H
Robinsons Best Bitter	H

Lively local with the accent on games. Good vault area with collection of photographs and paintings of the Manchester football teams.

ROMILEY ARMS
Stockport Road, SK6 4BN
NO REAL ALE

SPREAD EAGLE
Hatherlow, SK6 3DR
junction of Green Lane
11 - 11 Mon - Sat, 12 - 10.30 Sun

Boddingtons Bitter	H

Spacious pub on split-levels with the accent on food. Nice location alongside Hatherlow Chapel. One of Romiley's oldest pubs.

STOCK DOVE
94 Compstall Road, SK6 4DE
junction of Birch Avenue
not recorded

Boddingtons Bitter	H
Theakstons Bitter	H

Open-plan pub in the centre of Romiley with separate drinking areas and alcoves.

WINDS
110 Beacon Road, SK6 3ET
NO REAL ALE

SHAW HEATH

FLORIST
100 Shaw Heath, SK2 6QS
junction of Longshut Lane West
4 - 11 Mon - Wed, 1 - 11 Thu - Fri, 11 - 11 Sat, 12 - 3
& 7 - 10.30 Sun

Robinsons Hatters	H
Robinsons Best Bitter	H

Small-looking at first glance but actually has five rooms. Popular meeting venue for Stockport County fans.

PLOUGH
197 Shaw Heath, SK2 6QZ
NO REAL ALE

For a quart of Ale is dish for a King
- William Shakespeare, "Othello"

67

BREWING IN STOCKPORT   BY PETER SOANE

ALTHOUGH nowadays, Stockport has just one remaining brewery, *Robinsons*, this was not always the case. A century or so ago, the town boasted half a dozen sizeable breweries plus at least ten smaller ones, and prior to that, up to a hundred licensed public houses sold beer brewed on the premises.

One of the largest of the old breweries was *Bell & Co. Ltd*, situated on Hempshaw Lane, Offerton. Originally known as the Hempshaw Brook Brewery, it was owned by Avery Fletcher, a brush maker of Great Underbank. By 1909, Bell's had installed a new bottling plant which enabled the brewery to produce a beer that "did not throw down a deposit in the bottle", and a couple of years later, the chairman was able to report that the new bottled beer was selling very well. Bell's was eventually taken over by Robinson's on 25th March 1949 when cheques to the value of £65,000 were despatched to the shareholders of Bell and Co Ltd. Part of the brewery is still standing on Hempshaw Lane near the new junction with St. Mary's Way. Some former Bell's houses now in Robinson's livery include the Alexandra Hotel, Edgeley, the Blossoms, Buxton Rd and the Red Bull, Middle Hillgate.

At a cost of £7,000 and incorporating a well 75ft deep, *Charles Marsland* built a brewery near his residence, Brookfield House, just off Hempshaw Lane at the top of Christie Street. When work was completed in May of 1865, the opening was celebrated at the Three Jolly Carters Wellington Rd South. This building was converted to offices and the name on the front of the building has been changed from Brookfield 'Hotel' to 'House'. When Charles Marsland died in 1877, his wife Sarah carried on his kindness to his workers and instigated the yearly outing for her employees, which became quite an event in Stockport's social calendar. In May 1890, the brewery was sold

to Walter Showell and Co., and at the Annual General Meeting of Dec 9th 1897, the chairman of the new *Showell's Stockport Brewery Ltd.* was able to report a profit of £16,112. However, by 1907 profits were down, mainly due to compensation having to be paid to the owners and tenants of pubs that had been closed. Three years later, a proposal to amalgamate with *Walker and Homfray Ltd.* of Salford was carried unanimously at a shareholders meeting. Some former Marsland's houses include the Railway, Avenue St. (now a Porters pub), the Strawberry Gardens, Offerton Lane and the White House, Hempshaw Lane.

Although Richard Clarke from Butley, near Macclesfield, originally brewed beer at the Ash, Reddish, he started building *Clarke's Reddish Brewery* in South Reddish near St. Ann's School. His son, John Clarke, became more involved in the company and by the 1890's he was running the business with his brother Edward. Richard Clarke died in 1899 and a memorial service was held at Christ Church, Heaton Norris, which he had attended for 40 years. The company went from strength to strength, and as well as buying public houses, also built new ones, including the Ladybrook Hotel in Bramhall. However, in the early 1940s, talks were held with the owners of Bell's Brewery with a view to amalgamation, although shortly afterwards Harry Bell died and the idea was shelved. By the 1950's and 60's, smaller breweries were being swallowed up at an alarming rate by the big boys and Clarke's was no exception. Consequently, in December 1962, *Boddingtons Brewery* made a £1,000,000 offer for the company which was accepted by the shareholders on 24th January 1963. Sir Douglas Clarke J.P., head of the company at that time, rather naively described the takeover as a "very friendly affair" but in a more sinister vein, a Boddington's spokesman announced that their beers would be on sale in Clarke's 60 houses within 6 months. True to their word, on 20th June 1963, the last bottle of Clarke's beer left the brewery and a few hours later the century-old company closed down for good. Some former Clarke's houses include

the Black Lion, Hillgate, Crown Hotel, Heaton Moor Rd, Gardeners Arms, Offerton Lane and Kings Head, Tiviot Dale.

In the 1800's, there were many breweries operating on a much smaller scale than those previously mentioned. *The Chapel House*, Heaton Chapel, was built in 1822 and by 1828 boasted a new reception room for parties and also advertised a garden "for the accommodation of those who prefer the open air during the summer months". The ale was "homebrewed and of the finest quality and flavour". When the original lease on the Chapel House expired in 1888, the property was auctioned. Comprising of a smoke room, billiard room, tap room and two sitting rooms, it was "well cellared" and had stabling and a coach house. *Taylor's Eagle Brewery* paid £2,300 for the Chapel House and brewing ceased with the brew house being converted to other uses in the late 1890's.

Benjamin Smith opened the *Waterloo Brewery* on Hall St in 1825, and by the following decade he was supplying the George IV on Great Portwood St. By 1850, the business was trading as Henry Smith and Co., Waterloo Brewery and over the next few years made acquisitions such as the Magnet Inn, Heaton Norris, Moulders Arms, Daw Bank and the Greyhound, Bredbury. The brewery produced a "very superior article in table beer which they offer at 10d per gallon or casks of 9 and 18 gallons". The Waterloo Brewery was extended and modernised in the 1850's and 60's, with bottling capacity increased and more licensed houses acquired. Twenty years later the brewery's estate had grown considerably. The Waterworks Inn, the Mechanics Arms and the Church Inn, all Portwood, were just some of the purchases. The business appeared to have been very much a one-man concern and in January 1888 the Waterloo Brewery was advertised for sale as a going concern due to Benjamin Smith being in a poor state of health. When the auction took place at the Albion Hotel, Piccadilly, Manchester, apart from the brewing equipment there were over 3000 barrels, four draught horses and four drays and *Thomas Sykes and Co.* (later the *Trent Brewery Co.*) of Burton-On-Trent purchased the brewery and licensed houses. In July 1890, the Waterloo Brewery premises were sold and the building was demolished by 1895. A year later, all of the licensed property was sold when Thomas Sykes and Co. went into liquidation.

A few of the old brew houses are worth a specific mention with a couple of them still going strong, although no longer brewing.

The *Arden Arms*, Millgate, replaced an older property *"Ye Blew Stoops"* which was described as ancient in 1709. The Raffald family ran the *'Arderne Arms'* for over 80 years, handing the business down from father to son. Mrs Ann Raffald continued to run the pub and brew there after her husband's death in 1845. Regular brewing ceased in 1877, and the owner John Baker sold out to Robinson's Brewery in 1889.

According to an 1832 advertisement, the *Black Boy*, Great Underbank, was "the oldest established vault in the town" and had a "capital brew house with every convenience connected". In 1839, William Cooper took over and announced that his "home-brewed nut brown ale will bear the trust of the best judges". Three years later, John Foster acquired the Black Boy and brewing ceased.

On Newbridge lane, the *Coach and Horses* was brewing in 1824 and the business also included a bake house. Samuel Woodruffe, a well-known Stockport Brewer, was the proprietor in the late 1850's by which time there was a six-barrel brewery. When Woodruffe left a decade later brewing ceased, and although the pub became a spirits vaults for a time, it closed in 1886.

Finally, on Middle Hillgate, the *Sun and Castle* was mentioned in 1840 as having a brew house, which was extended in 1854 when the pub was described as having "an excellent vault with plate glass windows and brewing utensils in first-rate order". *Peter Walker and Sons* of Warrington later bought the pub which was rebuilt in the 1930's. After a period as a *Tetley's* pub, it is now owned by *Joseph Holt's* of Manchester.

STOCKPORT TOWN CENTRE

Arden Arms.   R.G. Edgecumbe.

ARDEN ARMS   T1

23 Millgate, SKI 2LY
Tel: 0161 480 2185
downhill from the Market Place
12 - II Mon - Sat, 12 - 10.30 Sun
Main Meals: 12 - 2.30 Mon - Sat, 12 - 4 Sun

Robinsons Hatters	**H**
Robinsons Best Bitter	**H**
Robinsons Old Tom (winter)	**H**
Robinsons Seasonal Guest	**H**

On CAMRA's National Inventory of classic pub interiors it is one of the finest examples of pub architecture in the North West, let alone Stockport. The Arden is always kept in tip-top decorative order with brown and cream walls, lots of wood, and plush, red furnishings. As well as its multi-room layout, it retains many fine features, including a superb glassed-in bar and chequerboard tiling. Entering from Corporation Street, there is a twin lounge on the right, divided by a folding wooden partition, while on the left, a drinking corridor winds around the bar to a further smart lounge. The finest room, and an increasingly rare feature in British pubs, is a small snug reached by asking permission and going through the bar servery! Together with Good Beer Guide quality beer, and superb food available at lunchtimes, (the licensees previously ran a highly-rated restaurant), this is truly an unmissable gem.

BAKERS VAULTS

Castle Yard, Market Place, SKI IES
II - II Mon - Tue, Thu - Sat. Closed Wed & Sun

Robinsons Hatters	**E**
Robinsons Best Bitter	**E**

Impressive Italianate pub with a high ceiling. One-roomed interior with large island bar. Food orientated.

BAMBOOZA

Market Place, St Petersgate, SKI IUN
NO REAL ALE

BISHOPS BLAIZE

63 Lower Hillgate, SKI 3AW
12 - II Mon - Sat, 12 - 3 & 7 - 10.30 Sun

Burtonwood Bitter	**H**
Burtonwood Top Hat	**H**

A 1930's house whose architecture merits its inclusion on CAMRA's National Inventory. The left hand two rooms, consisting of a large lounge with stage area and a separate snug/pool room, are at a lower level than the half-panelled, classic vault, with its leaded glass and pew seating. Entertainment at weekends. Pub games and Beer Garden.

BLACK LION

41 Middle Hillgate, SKI 3DG
NO REAL ALE

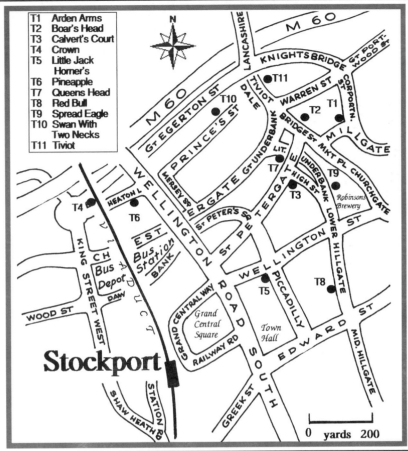

T1	Arden Arms
T2	Boar's Head
T3	Calvert's Court
T4	Crown
T5	Little Jack Horner's
T6	Pineapple
T7	Queens Head
T8	Red Bull
T9	Spread Eagle
T10	Swan With Two Necks
T11	Tiviot

0   yards   200

STOCKPORT RAIL VIADUCT
BY MARK MCCONACHIE

The 'Landmark' of Stockport. At 111 feet high, Stockport's railway viaduct is Western Europe's largest brick structure and represents a major feat of Victorian engineering. Eleven million bricks were used in the construction of its 27 arches - if laid end to end they would stretch 1,500 miles! To complete the massive structure, 600 workers were employed at one stage, working shifts, day and night. Completed in December 1840, the first passengers were carried on May 10th 1842 on the original two-track viaduct, with services running to Crewe, thus enabling travellers from Stockport to reach London. The west face was widened to give four tracks during 1887-89 to accommodate the increase in traffic. During 1989, in a £3 million restoration project (compared to an original cost of £70,000), the viaduct was floodlit and given a facelift. The structure is Grade II* listed and was awarded a blue plaque (one of only twelve in the Borough) to celebrate the Millennium; this can be viewed on the Daw Bank arch near the Bus Station.

71

BLARNEY STONE

55 St Petersgate, SKI IDH
junction of Piccadilly
11.30 - 11 Mon - Sat, 12 - 10.30 Sun

| Charles Wells Bombadier | H |

Irish theme pub with live entertainment evenings Mon - Sun and Saturday lunchtime. A wide range of food.

BOARS HEAD   T2

2 Vernon Street, Market Place, SKI IYT
Tel: 0161 480 3978
11 - 11 Mon - Sat, 12 - 10.30 Sun
*Main Meals: 11 - 4 Tue, Fri - Sat 12 - 3 Wed - Thu,
12 - 4 Sun*

| Samuel Smith Old Brewery Bitter | H |

Recently refurbished by Sam Smiths in a laudable manner, changing the pub from a featureless single room into a genuinely cosy city centre pub with a multi-room feel. While retaining much of its cosmopolitan clientele, the revamped pub now has a distinctly upmarket feel. The front room has been divided into a sparsely furnished 'public lounge' on the right (cleverly split into two areas) and a more substantial lounge containing a generous bar top, and comfortably furnished with a mix of cushioned pews, high-backed chairs and stools. The formerly bare back room is now used as a second lounge, served by a new extension to the bar. The pub now conforms to the brewery's no-live-music policy, it is a popular function venue. Lunchtime food is very popular on market days.

BRANNIGAN'S METRO

Grand Central Square, SKI 3TB
NO REAL ALE

BRIDGE ST WINE BAR

17 Bridge Street, SKI IXR
NO REAL ALE

BULLS HEAD

Market Place, SKI IEW
Closed Mon, 11.30 - 3 & 8 - 11.30 Tue, 8 - 11.30 Wed, 1 - 3
& 8 - 12 Thu, 11-3 & 8 - 1 Fri - Sat, 12 - 3 & 9 - 00.30 Sun

| Robinsons Hatters | H |
| Robinsons Best Bitter | H |

Large and cavernous opened-out music pub. High ceilings and simple furnishings. Home to live bands Tuesday to Thursday, some of which are distinctly loud.

CALVERTS COURT   T3

13 St Petersgate, SKI IEB
Tel: 0161 474 6750
near Stockport Market
10 - 11 Mon - Sat, 12 - 10.30 Sun
Main Meals: 10 - 10 Mon - Sat, 10 - 9.30 Sun

Boddingtons Bitter	H
Theakstons Best Bitter	H
Shepherd Neame Spitfire	H
Courage Directors	H
up to 5 Guest Beers	H

One of the most recent additions to Stockport's pub scene, Calverts Court was converted from a bed and furniture store. Much bigger than it looks on first impression, the standing area at the bar gives way to raised alcoves and comfortable chairs with a large dining area towards the rear, where you will also find a "No Smoking" area. A well-appointed courtyard at the rear of the building can be enjoyed on those rare English sunny days. A particularly welcome feature is the "Try before

you buy" policy. This pub has recently begun opening at 10.00 a.m. for coffee and breakfast, though of course normal licensing hours apply for alcohol. Thursday curry nights are especially popular and children are welcome to eat with their parents until 5.00 p.m. The pub can become very busy at weekends when the younger end of the market comes to town. Calverts Court takes its name from a group of houses which stood nearby in the early 20th Century, one of which was owned by W. Calvert, Cabinet Maker.

CHESTERGATE TAVERN
66 Chestergate, SK1 1NP
NO REAL ALE

COBDENS
25 Wellington Road South, SK4 1AA
junction of St Petersgate
12 - 8 Mon, 12 - 11 Tue - Thu, 12 - 2am Fri - Sat, closed Sun

Robinsons Best Bitter	H
Robinsons Seasonal Guest	H

Predominently young persons trendy, venue style pub with emphasis on music and extended opening.

CROWN
14 Higher Hillgate, SK1 3ER
NO REAL ALE

CROWN INN   T4
154 Heaton Lane, SK4 1AR
Tel: 0161 429 0549
off roundabout, junction of Gt Egerton St.
12 - 3 & 6 - 11 Mon - Thu, 12.30 - 11 Fri - Sat, 7.30 - 10.30 Sun
Bar Snacks: 12 - 2 & Early Evening (Mon - Fri),
Main Meals: 12 - 2 Mon - Fri

Jennings Bitter	H
Up to 9 Guest Beers	H
Guest Cider	G

This pub has appeared on the cover of all three editions of this guide, partly due to its striking location under Stockport's landmark railway viaduct. However; it is also one of the town's foremost cask ale houses. Up to ten are usually available plus a traditional cider. House policy is to always have a cask mild available, plus at least one beer from local brewers Phoenix, Bank Top, Pictish and Whim. Its impressive facade leads to a five-roomed gem, comprising front and rear snugs (the latter non-smoking), bar, plush lounge and pool room. All this is topped off with a large, irregularly shaped yard, which is variously used as a beer garden, music venue and barbecue area - sometimes all at once! Music plays a large part in the pubs itinerary, with live events four nights a week featuring rock, folk, acoustic and more. Decor is similarly varied with rock star photos and music scores in the pool room, copperware and a huge overmantel in the lounge.

CUBE
Grand Central Square, SK1 3TA
NO REAL ALE

ALWAYS REMEMBER THAT I HAVE TAKEN MORE OUT OF ALCOHOL THAN ALCOHOL HAS TAKEN OUT OF ME.
-WINSTON CHURCHILL

73

EGERTON ARMS

2 St Petersgate, SK1 1HD
II - II Mon - Wed, II - 12.30 Thu, II - I Fri - Sat, 12 - 12 Sun

Boddingtons Bitter	H
Tetley Bitter	H

Fairly unremarkable with smallish lounge and pool room. The extended weekend hours usually host karaoke/disco evenings.

GEORGE HOTEL

15 Wellington Road North, SK4 1AF
NO REAL ALE

GOLDEN LION

89 Middle Hillgate, SK1 3EH
NO REAL ALE

KINGS HEAD

11 Tiviot Dale, SK1 1TA
just off Princes St, opposite Tiviot
II.30 - II Mon - Thu, II - II Fri - Sat, 12 - 10.30 Sun

Worthington Best Bitter	H
Draught Bass	H
Guest Beer	H

Traditional town pub with long wood-panelled room. Large screen TV for football.

LAMP HOTEL

62 - 64 Middle Hillgate, SK1 3EH
NO REAL ALE

LITTLE JACK HORNERS   T5

28 Lord Street, SK1 3NA
Tel: 0161 477 3086
junction of Wellington Street
II.30 - II Mon - Fri, 12 - 4 & 7 - II Sat, 12 - 3 & 7 - 10.30 Sun
Main Meals: 12 - 2 Mon - Fri

Worthington Bitter	H
Tetley Bitter	H
Marstons Pedigree	H
Camerons Strongarm	H

Situated within easy reach of Stockport railway station, this is a well appointed traditional three roomed pub. It appears externally to be rather narrow and small, however there are three

linked but separate drinking areas. It has a thriving lunchtime office trade, providing excellent food, and a loyal regular evening trade, especially at weekends. It has a friendly atmosphere with tastefully understated background music for ease of quiet conversation.

NELSON TAVERN

98 Wellington Road South, SK1 3UH
junction of Greek Street
II.30 - II Mon - Fri, 12 - II Sat, 12 - 10.30 Sun

Theakstons Best Bitter	H
Guest Beer	H

Attracting a young clientele, the interior is bright and open plan with a central bar. A plaque outside gives a history of the pub.

OLD RECTORY

48 Churchgate, SK1 1YG
II - II Mon - Sat, 12 - 10.30 Sun

Theakstons Bitter	H
Guest Beer(s)	H

Rebuilt in the 17th century. Previously the home to the Bishops of Stockport.

PACK HORSE

2 Market Place, SK1 1EW
II - II Mon - Sat, 12 - 10.30 Sun

Tetley Bitter	H
Ansells Bitter	H

Multi-roomed pub of considerable character opposite Stockport parish church, which itself is worth a visit.

PINEAPPLE   T6

159 Heaton Lane, SK4 1AQ
Tel: 0161 480 3221
near junction of Wellington Road North
II.30 - II Mon - Sat, 12 - 4 & 7 - 10.30 Sun
Bar Snacks: All Day, Main Meals: 11.30 - 2 Mon - Sun

Robinsons Hatters	E
Robinsons Best Bitter	E
Robinsons Seasonal Guest	H
Robinsons Old Tom (seasonal)	H

The Pineapple became a Public House in the late 1820s though the actual building is considerably older. Originally a coaching house, it became the headquarters of Stockport Botanical Society before being purchased by Bells in 1904. It is a traditional local, in the centre of a busy shopping and industrial area. With its timber beamed roof, and its walls decorated with ornamental crockery from all over the world, this little gem always has a warm, friendly atmosphere with prompt and efficient service. Handy for the Hat Museum.

THE PINEAPPLE

THE QUEEN'S HEAD (TURNERS VAULTS)

PURE
21 Fletcher Street, SK1 1DY
NO REAL ALE

QUEENS HEAD T7
12 Little Underbank, SK1 1JT
Tel: 0161 480 0725
11 - 11 Mon - Sat, 12 - 7 Sun
Bar Snacks: 12 - 2.30 Mon - Sat
  Samuel Smith Old Brewery Bitter **H**

Walking into the Queens Head, from the Underbank conservation area, you would think that you were walking back in time to the 19th Century and yet the pub was actually completely rebuilt internally in the early '90s. Sam Smiths did such a superb job that this is architecturally one of the truly great pubs in the guide. It is known locally as Turners Vaults, relating to its 19th Century function as the tasting room for Turner's Wine Merchants. The pub has a nar-

row frontage yet such is the depth of the place it is surprisingly sizeable. The first of three rooms going back is the wooden floored bar area with its bench seating. The bar itself has an arc of old spirit taps which are worth looking at while you order a pint. After you have made your way through the bar, which can be difficult when the pub is busy, you will find the news room which is actually an alcove set back from the corridor leading to the lounge at the rear. The news room has bench seating and brass rods on which the papers are hung. Two further interesting features are the "Compacto" which is supposed to be the world's smallest Gents and the haunted room at the top of the stairs leading to the toilets. Both are locked but will be opened on request (the "Compacto" is a favourite photo opportunity for American tourists). If you don't visit this pub when you visit Stockport then you have really missed a gem!

It was the accepted practice in Babylon 4,000 years ago that for a month after the wedding, the bride's father would supply his son-in-law with all the mead he could drink. Mead is a honey beer, and because their calendar was lunar based, this period was called the "honey month", or what we know today as the "honeymoon".

SAM'S BAR
26 - 7 Market Place, SK1 1ES
NO REAL ALE

RED BULL   T8
14 Middle Hillgate, SK1 3AY
Tel: 0161 480 2087
11.30 - 11 Mon - Sat, 12 - 3 & 7 - 10.30 Sun
Bar Snacks: 12 - 4.30 Mon - Sat, Main Meals: 12 - 3 Mon - Sat

Robinsons Hatters	H
Robinsons Best Bitter	H

The Red Bull is often described as a 'country pub in a town setting'. It is a whitewashed building with the entrance up some well-worn steps. There is also a splendid interior with dark wood, served by a large three-sided bar, and all with the look and feel of a country pub. There are an assortment of areas in the pub, including a traditional stone-flagged snug with pew seating, and a plusher lounge snug which has a real fire in winter and its own bar for very busy times. Bric-a-brac around the pub include mirrors, brass ornaments and pictures and drawings of old Stockport. The Red Bull is popular with Robinson's directors (especially lunchtimes where the pub is renowned for its high quality food) and very busy in the evenings. A Folk Club is held on Monday nights in the Upper Bar, and a Jazz Club - approx every two months.

ROYAL OAK HOTEL
11 High Street, SK1 1EG
just off the bridge connecting St Petersgate to the Market
11 - 11 Mon - Sat, 12 - 10.30 Sun

Robinsons Hatters	E
Robinsons Best Bitter	E

Basically one room divided into three areas. 'Take away' chicken curry available at all times as well as good value lunchtime food (not Monday).

SPREAD EAGLE   T9
Lower Hillgate, SK1 1JQ
Tel: 0161 480 7057
adjacent to Robinson's Brewery
11 - 11 Mon - Sat, 7.30 - 10.30 Sun
Bar Snacks: 12 - 2 Mon - Sat

Robinsons Hatters	E
Robinsons Best Bitter	E
Robinsons Old Tom (winter)	E

The Robinsons Brewery tap, whose main distinction is that it stands on the site of the original Unicorn Inn where Frederic Robinson first started brewing. Much altered internally, a loyal band of regulars and brewery workers create a lively community atmosphere. Old Tom is available in antique nip glasses for those with too much sense to drink halves. There is a compact pool room and darts is often played immediately by the front door, which can be disconcerting. As well as low prices, the pub offers a delicious range of home-made curries which can be taken away.

STAR AND GARTER
61 Higher Hillgate, SK1 3HD
12 - 11 Mon - Sat, 12 - 10.30 Sun

Robinsons Hatters	H
Robinsons Best Bitter	H
Robinsons Old Tom	G

Opened out but with clearly separate areas within the lounge. At the back is a separate vault.

STOCKPORT ARMS

25 St Petersgate, SK1 1EB
11.30 - 11 Mon - Sat, 7 - 10.30 Sun

Greenalls Bitter	H
Tetley Bitter	H

A traditional environment with value lunches. Fri/Sat eves see a female DJ host a disco. Plans for an outside drinking area.

SUN AND CASTLE

54 Middle Hillgate, SK1 3DL
100 yards south of Edward Street junction
11 - 11 Mon - Sat, 12 - 10.30 Sun

Holt Mild	H
Holt Bitter	H

Long vault, large lounge and snug. Good example of Holt's 'traditional' style of decor.

SWAN WITH TWO NECKS   T10

36 Princes Street, SK1 1RY
Tel: 0161 480 2341
11 - 11 Mon - Sat, closed Sun
Main Meals: 11.30 - 2 Mon - Sat

Robinsons Hatters	H
Robinsons Best Bitter	H
Robinsons Frederics	H
Robinsons Old Tom (seasonal)	H
Robinsons Seasonal Guest	H

The Swan With Two Necks is the only pub remaining on Princes Street, one of Stockport's main town-centre shopping streets, now pedestrianised. It has a narrow frontage adorned by mock half-timbering, but the three-room interior goes back a long way and is surprisingly roomy. It was remodelled in the 1920s, making extensive use of light oak panelling, and has changed very little since then. As a rare survivor of an authentic refit of that period it appears on CAMRA's National Inventory of historic pub interiors. Pride of place goes to the superb wood-panelled, top-lit snug at the heart of the pub, which must be a strong contender for the finest pub room in Stockport, and which provides the perfect escape from the bustle of the shopping centre.

After a period when it seemed to lose its way, the Swan was taken over by a new and more enterprising licensee a few years ago, who extended the opening hours and the food menu and started to offer a variety of other beers from Robinson's range to complement the standard Hatters Mild and Best Bitter. Because of its location in the shopping centre the pub tends to be

Swan With Two Necks.

busier at lunchtimes than in the evening, but it has a loyal band of regulars and often hosts meetings of clubs and societies. Tuesday night features a regular pub quiz. There is a large public car park at the rear which is free in the evenings.

THATCHED HOUSE

74 Churchgate, SK1 1YS
300 yards from the market
5-11 Mon - Sun

Boddingtons Bitter	H
Coors Worthington Bitter	H
Morland Old Speckled Hen	H

The 'Tudor' style exterior belies the basic interior and mixture of heavy rock and real ale that attracts the clientele.

THREE SHIRES WINE BAR

30 - 32 Great Underbank, SK1 1NB
NO REAL ALE

The original text of the Reinheitsgebot (the ancient German beer purity law inaugurated in 1516) only allowed three ingredients: Barley, hops, and water. Yeast wasn't mentioned for another 35 years.

all the good things well. Ink drawings of town centre pubs adorn the lounges and steam loco prints (a reminder of the nearby, but demolished, Tiviot Dale station) decorate the vault. Good value food at lunchtimes (Tue to Sat), quieter in evening. Present licensee has held the licence for over 25 years, before that he served as barman under his father, the previous licensee, for a dozen years.

TOWN HALL TAVERN
95 Wellington Road South, SK1 3SL
NO REAL ALE

UNITY
41 Wellington Road South, SK1 3PU
corner of Wellington Street
12 - 11 Mon - Sat, 12 - 10.30 Sun

Robinsons Hatters	H
Robinsons Best Bitter	H

Town centre pub with a good local feel. Typically 'Robinsonised' inside but retains attractive exterior. Lunchtime food.

WATERLOO
8-10 Waterloo Road, SK1 3BD
11.30 - 11 Mon - Sat, 12 - 10.30 Sun

Robinsons Hatters	E
Robinsons Best Bitter	E

Just off Hillgate opposite the site of the 1967 Stockport Air Disaster. Has a well-furnished lounge, a vault, games room and a snug.

WHITE LION
20 Great Underbank, SK1 1LW
NO REAL ALE

WINTERS
Little Underbank, SK1 1LA
11 - 11 Mon - Sat, 12 - 10.30 Sun

Holt Mild	H
Holt Bitter	H

Holts created the pub out of former jewellers (J. Winters) and skilfully left much of the exterior intact including the automaton clock, one of Stockport's landmarks.

TIVIOT   T11
8 Tiviot Dale, SK1 1TA
Tel: 0161 480 4109
just off the eastern end of Princes Street
11 - 11 Mon - Sat, 12 - 3.30 Sun
Main Meals: 12 - 2 Tues - Sat

Robinsons Hatters	E
Robinsons Best Bitter	E
Robinsons Old Tom (winter)	G

Busy town centre pub, serving a mixture of locals and shoppers. A lively vault has its own entrance at the front, and there is a comfortable lounge on the right, a longer room with seating and table football behind, and a dining room off the long drinking corridor. A simple community pub, doing

STRINES

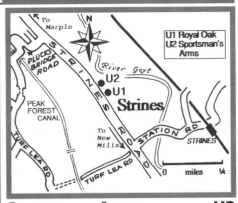

ROYAL OAK U1

121 Strines Road, SK6 7GE
Tel: 0161 427 6354
1/4 mile south of Plucksbridge Road jct.
Buses: 358
12 - 3 & 5.30 - 11 Mon - Sat, 12 - 3 & 7.30 - 10.30 Sun
Main Meals: 12 - 2 & 5.30 - 9 Wed - Sun,
No Food Mon - Tue

Robinsons Hatters	H
Robinsons Best Bitter	H
Robinsons Old Tom (winter)	G
Robinsons Seasonal Guest (occasional)	H

Low, cottage pub that backs on to the Goyt Valley and gives scenic views over to Mellor Moor and beyond. Inside one finds three small, low-ceilinged rooms. On the left is a tiny tap room with T.V., a period cash register and dartboard, and locally produced free range eggs. The middle room contains the main bar, with a real fire, two picture windows, settle seating and Britannia tables. Ask to see the 'Log.' To the right, is the cosy dining room offering good value fare. At the time of going to press, building work will extend the dining room and provide a patio/drinking area. The pub plays host to a lively social programme - from 'Rollocks' nights (ask!), to pub and curry crawls and regional food evenings. Check the events calendar in the bar for that month's details.

SPORTSMANS ARMS U2

105 Strines Road, SK6 7GE
Tel: 0161 427 2888
1/4 mile south of Plucksbridge Road jct.
Buses: 358
12 - 3 & 5.30 - 11 Mon - Sat, 12 - 3 & 7 - 10.30 Sun
Main Meals: 12 - 2 & 6 - 9 Daily

Cains Mild	H
Cains Bitter	H
Boddingtons Bitter	H
Two Guest Beers	H

Originally a private dwelling dating from about 1790, it gained its first licence circa 1805 to become an ale house known as 'Sport House'. It has had a chequered existence over the years, mostly providing for the Navigators building the nearby canals and then the subsequent canal users. This welcoming pub has two rooms; a vault and a large lounge catering mostly for diners. The present landlord has re-opened a large ingle-nook fireplace and fitted a huge picture window with superb views over to Mellor. The pub has a strong accent on good quality home made food.

WOODFORD

DAVENPORT ARMS V1
550 Chester Road, SK7 1PS
Tel: 0161 439 2435
on A5102 near junction of Church Lane
Buses: Terminus of 157 (from M/cr, Cheadle, Cheadle Hulme and Bramhall)
11 - 3.30 & 5.15 - 11 Mon - Fri, 11 - 11 Sat, 12 - 3 & 7 - 10.30 Sun
Main Meals: 12 - 2 Sun - Fri, 12 - 3 Sat

Robinsons Hatters	H
Robinsons Best Bitter	H
Robinsons Seasonal Guest	H
Robinsons Old Tom (winter)	H

Stockport is a mainly urban area with few real country pubs, so it's a pleasant surprise that among that handful there is one of the very best. Better known to many as the "Thief's Neck", the Davenport Arms externally has the aspect of an old-fashioned Cheshire farmhouse, built of mellow red brick and surrounded by rambling outbuildings. The exterior features impressive floral displays in Spring and Summer.

Inside, the pub has kept its small, cosy rooms. On the left is a plain but cosy tap room, focused on the dartboard and featuring some interesting old "Farmer's Weekly" posters of British livestock. On the right is a comfortable snug where children are welcome at lunchtimes. This is now a no-smoking area which has proved a very popular feature. To the rear is a combined lounge/ bar area where drinkers tend to cluster thickly around the counter.

The atmosphere is firmly traditional, With no piped music, apart perhaps from the radio being played at low volume at quiet times, no pool table, and three blazing real fires in winter. The pub's location on the edge of prosperous "stockbroker belt" areas is reflected in some of its clientele, but it is used by a wide cross-section of society, and remains genuinely unpretentious and welcoming to all. Its location close to Woodford's British Aerospace factory, where the famous Lancaster and Vulcan bombers were produced, explains the aviation photographs and memorabilia scattered throughout the pub. Good, mostly home-made food is served at lunchtimes, with traditional staples complemented by some more adventurous dishes. At the rear, adjoining the local cricket pitch and well away from the main road, is one of Stockport's best pub gardens, an ideal spot for families where children will appreciate the farmyard livestock. The forecourt offers an alternative outdoor drinking area, and both these facilities are well-used in summer.

The Davenport Arms was acquired by Robinson's in the 1920s, and since then the licence has been held by four successive generations of the Hallworth family, a record of continuity which is unique in the Stockport area. The pub is a former holder of CAMRA's Greater Manchester Pub of the Year title and in 2003 celebrates sixteen consecutive years in CAMRA's national Good Beer Guide. When so many pubs in the surrounding area have been converted

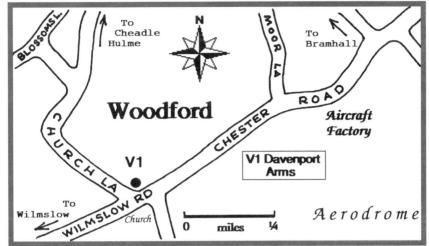

to identikit dining establishments it remains a bastion of tradition and quality. A true classic pub and one definitely not to be missed.

DO NOT CEASE TO DRINK BEER, TO EAT, TO INTOXICATE THYSELF, TO MAKE LOVE AND TO CELEBRATE THE GOOD DAYS.
- ANCIENT EGYPTIAN CREDO

WOODLEY

LOWES ARMS
18 Hyde Road, SK6 1QG
12 - 11 Mon - Sat, 12 - 10.30 Sun
Robinsons Hatters	E
Robinsons Best Bitter	E

A modern 60s/70s affair at the west end of the precinct.

NAVIGATION
134 Hyde Road, SK6 1NL
12 - 3.30 & 5.30 - 11 Mon - Fri, 12 - 11 Sat, 12 - 10.30 Sun
Robinsons Hatters	E
Robinsons Best Bitter	E

Quality leaded windows and a somewhat Georgian appearance, a lozenge-shaped bar divides vault from lounge and a separate, well-appointed, front snug. Ornate Adam-style decorative motifs atop the bar canopy in the lounge.

RAILWAY
168 Hyde Road, SK6 1NL
4 - 11 Mon - Fri, 12 - 11 Sat, 12 - 10.30 Sun
Robinsons Hatters	H
Robinsons Best Bitter	H

Good sized, comfy lounge to right with a somewhat intrusive bar; separate Tap Room to left with an emphasis on darts and doms.

WAGON & HORSES
Woodley Precinct, SK6 1RJ
NO REAL ALE

WHITE HART
170 Hyde Road, SK6 1NP
NO REAL ALE

MARPLE RAIL VIADUCT

BY MARK McCONACHIE

This lies just north of Marple Wharf Junction, running parallel to Marple Aqueduct and carries rail traffic from Manchester to Sheffield on the Hope Valley line and also locally to Rose Hill; and onward to Macclesfield in bygone days. Towering 130 feet above the River Goyt, it provides the link between Marple and Romiley. Taking a year to build, it was completed in 1863, but only opened to traffic on July 1st 1865. Consisting of 12 rusticated stone arches, it is best viewed from the Peak Forest Canal towpath.

BEER AND BREWERIES FEATURED

BY ROBIN WIGNALL

IN addition to a clutch of microbreweries within and around the county, Greater Manchester is also blessed with a handful of good regional family brewers, not to mention one brewing factory owned by an international company that still brews cask beer. Other national and multi-national brewers also supply their products to the region.

THE LOCAL INDEPENDENT

ROBINSONS, STOCKPORT

Here in Stockport, Robinson's is a large family-owned regional brewer. Established in 1838, the Robinson's estate now boasts over 400 pubs in an area from Greater Manchester to North Wales and from the Potteries to South Cumbria. Pubs in the last area were acquired as a result of the take over of Hartley's of Ulverston, now closed, and the accompanying estate. Robinson's is still very much a family operation with continuity into the younger generation of the dynasty ensuring its future independence. Brewing takes place at the town centre site, whilst racking and bottling have now moved to the large facility at Bredbury. Upgrading and modernisation of brewing plant has not precluded Robinson's from continuing as a very traditional brewer. At their best, the cask beers are fine brews that have regularly won awards from CAMRA and other organisations. Amongst these was Cask Champion, conferred recently by the local CAMRA branch in recognition of the brewery's Best Kept Bar and Cellar competition, designed to raise the consistency and quality of cask ale in the company's tied estate, and also for the establishment of seasonal beers, a number of which have been quite outstanding.

Hatters (3.3%) - Dry and malty. Previously called Best Mild.

Dark Mild (3.3%) - Hatters with added caramel. Very rare.

Old Stockport (3.5%) - Formerly just known as Bitter. Soft and fruity session beer. Limited availability but worth seeking out.

Best Bitter (4.2%) - The best seller. An amber brew with a good balance of malt and hops.

Frederic's (5.0%) - A pale, hoppy, single- varietal premium beer. Not widely available in Stockport for some bizarre reason.

Old Tom (8.5%) - Award-winning rich, dark, strong winter brew. Available in a few stalwart outlets throughout the year.

Hartley's XB (4.0%) - Some cynics might say remarkably similar to Best Bitter. Brewed mainly for the ex-Hartley's Cumbrian estate and rare in the Stockport area.

Hartley's Cumbria Way (4.1%) - Pale and hoppy session bitter mostly for Cumbria.

Seasonal Beers - change every two months

THE REGIONAL INDEPENDENTS

HYDES, MANCHESTER

Traditional brewer and previous winner of the Cask Champion award, mainly for its recent re-invigoration of its approach to cask beer. Almost uniquely in modern times, it produces three cask milds, two of which are regularly available in the Stockport area.

Light (3.5%) - A pale refreshing mild.

Mild (3.5%) - A mid-brown, malty beer.

Bitter (3.8%) - Smooth, full-bodied session beer.

Jekyll's Gold (4.3%) - Pale, hoppy and full-flavoured.

Seasonal Beers - change every two months

HOLTS, MANCHESTER

A brewery with a reputation for distinctive, full-flavoured ales and a keen pricing policy. Although still fairly rare, Holts have a bigger presence in Stockport compared with a few years ago. Some recent experimenting with seasonal/occasional brews.

Mild (3.2%) - Rich, dark and malty. Although toned down in recent years, still more bitter than some bitters.

Bitter (4.0%) - The CAMRA Good Beer Guide says "uncompromising bitterness can be a shock to the unwary". Enough said!

LEES, MIDDLETON JUNCTION, GTR. MANCHESTER

Another of the region's excellent family-owned independents but sadly with limited representation in Stockport. One local tied house (Travellers Call, Bredbury) and occasional appearances in the free trade.

GB Mild (3.5%) - A well-rounded, malty, sweetish brew.

Bitter (4.0%) - Pale and very distinctive with unusual hop flavours.

Moonraker (7.5%) - A rich, strong, dark, full-flavoured mainly winter ale. Not for the faint hearted.

Seasonal Beers - change every two months

THE OTHER INDEPENDENTS

Intermittent visitors to the free trade include Adnams (Southwold, Suffolk), Charles Wells (Bedford) and Shepherd Neame (Faversham, Kent).

SAMUEL SMITH, TADCASTER

Yorkshire's oldest brewery. A fiercely independant regional brewery with two tied houses in the central Stockport area. Only produce a single real ale which is still supplied in wooden casks.

Old Brewery Bitter (4.0%) - Viscous, malty brew with a dry flavour and bitter finish.

TIMOTHY TAYLOR, KEIGHLEY

Much-loved, multi-award-winning, enduring West Yorkshire brewers. No tied pubs near here but oft-represented in the free trade. Landlord is their flagship brew but some of their other offerings do occasionally sneak into the more discerning hostelries.

Landord (4.3%) - At its best, a superb example of how to balance malt and hops. Surely an indisputable 'desert island' beer.

JENNINGS, COCKERMOUTH

Locally, restricted to the free trade and pubco guest lists. Occasional rarities are Mild (3.1%), Cumberland Ale (4.0%), Cockerhoop (4.6%) and Snecklifter (5.1%).

Bitter (3.5%) - Darkish, malty and distinctive. Surprisingly full-bodied for a low gravity session beer.

BURTONWOOD (THOMAS HARDY BURTONWOOD LTD), WARRINGTON

Only three pubs in the Stockport area and one of these is keg. A few occasional/seasonal brews.

Bitter (3.7%) - Soft, easy-drinking session beer with some fruitiness.

Top Hat (4.8%) - Full-bodied, malty premium beer.

CAINS, LIVERPOOL

Housed in a splendid, ornate brewery building, more famously trading as Higson's in previous times. A recent takeover has hopefully assured the company's future. Has built up a small estate in Liverpool and has one tied house (Gothic Bar and Grill, Gatley) in this area, although the beers feature fairly regularly in the free trade.

Dark Mild (3.2%) - A smooth, dry, nutty mild.

Traditional Bitter (4.0%) - Darkish, sweetish and fairly hoppy.

FA (Formidable Ale) (5.0%) - A well-balanced, full-flavoured, hoppy premium beer. Dangerously drinkable.

HARDY AND HANSON (*KIMBERLEY*), *NOTTS.*

Rarely gets this far north but does have one local tied outlet (Governor's House, Cheadle Hulme)

Kimberley Best Bitter (3.9%) - Bitter-sweet and hoppy session beer.

Kimberley Classic (4.8%) - A premium bitter with plenty of hops.

Seasonal Beers

THE MICROBREWERIES

Stockport is well served by small brewers. Two of them have pubs in the borough, whilst others feature regularly in the free trade, including Phoenix (Heywood), Bank Top (Bolton), Pictish (Rochdale), Whim (Hartington, Derbyshire) and Black Sheep (Masham, Yorkshire).

PORTER'S, *ROSSENDALE*

Available at the award-winning, CAMRA Good Beer Guide listed Railway, Portwood. An extensive range is brewed by the long-established and redoubtable Dave Porter.

Dark Mild (3.3%) - A proper dark mild with rich, roasted malt flavours in abundance.

Floral Dance (3.6%) - A pale, refreshing session bitter with complex aromatic hop elements.

Bitter (3.7%) - A rich, darkish full-flavoured.

Railway Sleeper (4.2%) - Intensely bitter and hoppy. Brewed especially for the Railway.

Rossendale Ale (4.2%) - Less hoppy and more malty than most Porter beers.

Porter (5.0%) - Suberb, rich, roasted, full-flavoured and well-balanced. Dangerous!

Sunshine (5.3%) - Very pale, no-nonsense, 'in your face', full-frontal hop attack.

Stout (5.5%) - Black, full-bodied, very bitter, old-fashioned stout. Regarded by many local aficionados as the pick of the Porter beers.

Seasonal/Occasional Beers

BEARTOWN, *CONGLETON*

After gradually building up its operation, this brewery is now a welcome regular addition to the Stockport drinking scene. Many examples from this brewer's splendid range can be sampled at the Navigation, Heaton Norris.

Ambeardexterous (3.5%) - Dark mild.

Bear Ass (3.8%) - Good balance of malt and hops.

Kodiak Gold (4.0%) - Long-established best seller. Straw-coloured, creamy, hoppy bitter.

Bearskinful (4.2%) - Full-bodied, tasty session beer.

Polar Eclipse ((4.8%) - Roasted, dry stout.

Wheat Bear (5.0%) - Dry, bitter, wheat beer.

Seasonal/Occasional Beers

THE NATIONALS

WOLVERHAMPTON AND DUDLEY, *WEST MIDLANDS*

Brewers of Banks's beers and owners of Marston's brewery. Recently closed Mansfield Brewery, despite a legacy from the previous owners that bound the trustees to a sworn obligation to protect the company and workers jobs from oblivion.

Banks's Original (3.5%) - Lightweight, fruity erstwhile mild.

Banks's Bitter (3.8%) - Pale brown, sweetish and malty.

Marston's Pedigree (4.5%) - Frequent guest. Smooth, fruity premium bitter.

GREENE KING, *BURY ST EDMUNDS*

Feature regularly on pubco guest lists. Also own the Morland and Ruddles brands.

Abbot Ale (5.0%) - Full-bodied and clean tasting but a shadow of its former self.

Morland Old Speckled Hen (5.2%) - Dark and thin with pronounced alcoholic element.

Ruddles County (4.3%) - Much-travelled, much-altered, widely-touted. Thickish, malty and sweet. Bears no resemblance to its once distinctive original namesake.

THE MULTI-NATIONALS

CARLSBERG-TETLEY, *LEEDS*

Tetley Bitter (3.7%) - Ubiquitous. Soft. Unchallenging

Tetley Dark Mild (3.2%) - Ordinary mild with added caramel. Soft and sweetish but palatable.

Burton Ale (4.8%) - Another much-travelled descendant of Ind Coope's once magnificent, hoppy, distinctive beer. The current version is thinnish, soft and unremarkable.

Greenall's Bitter (3.8%) - Lightly-hopped. Soft, malty, sweet.

Ansell's Best Bitter (3.7%) - Soft and sweet.

INTERBREW, *MANCHESTER*

This multi-national corporation is the perpetrator of current day Boddington's. The modern members of this legendary local brewing dynasty sold the family jewels many moons ago to ex-brewers Whitbread who eventually hived it off to the present owners. It's getting increasingly difficult to tell the difference between the cask, keg, smoothflow and tinned versions of the ubiquitous Boddington's Bitter. After meandering all over the country, the Flower's beers are probably currently brewed at Boddington's.

Boddington's Bitter (3.8%) - Soft, smooth, unchallenging.

Flower's IPA (4.1%) - Thin and sweet.

Flowers Original (4.3%) - Thinish and sweet.

COORS, *BURTON ON TRENT*

Another recent foreign interloper on the once great British brewing scene. Managed to nab most of the Bass brands when Interbrew fell foul of the competition laws. Perversely, Draught Bass is actually brewed by Coors for Interbrew.

Worthington Bitter (3.6%) - Thin, soft, sweet, pale brown bitter.

Draught Bass (4.4%) - Once magnificent when brewed in the legendary Burton Union System. Now usually thin and sweet.

SCOTTISH COURAGE, *EDINBURGH/TADCASTER/TYNE*

Increasingly gaining market share and spreading out across Europe.

John Smith's Bitter (3.8%) - Soft, cloying, ubiquitous.

Webster's Green Label (3.2%) - Almost flavourless, originally a pale, smooth mild,

Courage Director's (4.8%) - This once magnificent, superbly-crafted, hoppy beer was originally so good that it was reserved as a private tipple for the directors of the brewery. The current version is soft, malty, thickish and sweet.

Theakston's Best Bitter (3.6%) - Dry and metallic.

Theakston's Cool Cask (4.2%) - Recently introduced for youngsters who don't really like the taste of beer.

Theakston's Mild (3.6%) - Thin. Rare.

MASTER INDEX - FEATURED PUBS IN BOLD TYPE

$YOU'RE$ *NOT DRUNK IF YOU CAN LIE ON THE*
FLOOR WITHOUT HOLDING ON.

-DEAN MARTIN

RECOMMENDED PUB CRAWL BY PETER SOANE

This pleasant stroll around central Stockport gives the visitor an opportunity to stretch their legs and sample a variety of beers in some of the town's finest pubs.

Starting at the **Swan With Two Necks*** on Princes Street, part of the main shopping precinct just minutes away from Mersey Square, this multi-roomed Robinson's pub has an impressive interior dating from the 1920's. Carrying on down Princes Street, pause for a minute to have a look at the mural on the BhS building. At the bottom of Princes St. is another Robinson's pub, **The Tiviot***, a multi-roomed pub including a separate vault. On leaving the pub, turn right past the church, then right again following the road behind the supermarket, then turn left at the traffic lights until you reach **The Railway*** on the left. Do not miss this award-winning pub owned by Dave Porter.

For the next pub on our walk, go back to the traffic lights and turn left, then at the mini roundabout you will find the **Arden Arms***. A Robinson's house, this Grade II listed building has many unusual features and under the current licencee is back to its best after a spell in the doldrums.

On leaving the Arden, turn right, right again, and left up to the market place where the newly refurbished **Boars Head** (Sam Smiths) is located.

From the Boars head, proceed forward keeping the in-door market on your left. Just before crossing the high-level bridge, go down the steps on the left and the **Queens Head** (Sam Smiths) is found directly opposite. Winner of the coveted Joe Goodwin award in 1991 for most sensitive conservation, the Queens Head is another ancient pub full of unusual features.

A few yards up Underbank is one of Stockport's few Holts pubs, **Winters**, recently converted from a jeweller's shop, with the workings of the original jeweller's clock still visible in the upstairs bar. Slightly further up the hill is the impressive sight of Robinsons Brewery on the left, and just before the main gates, is **The Spread Eagle***, the brewery tap and last pub on our crawl.

If you have visited all eight pubs on this tour of Stockport Town centre, you will have sampled beers from four independent breweries sold at very competitive prices. This is not a coincidence, as healthy competition beats monopoly every time and can only benefit the customer. So, let's raise our glasses to all the breweries that contribute to Stockport's richly diverse drinking scene, and long may it continue.

* *denotes entry in CAMRA 2003 Good Beer Guide*

JOIN THE CAMPAIGN FOR REAL ALE

Love beer or cider? Want to protect it as well as drink it? Want to make sure you can continue to enjoy your favourite pint of real ale in your local pub? Well, you may be interested to know that's what CAMRA is trying to ensure. We are one of the most successful consumer organisations in the country. We are Britain's **only** organisation dedicated to promoting the interests of the beer and cider drinker. We campaign to help protect consumer rights, promote quality, choice and value for money as well as campaigning to save local pubs and independent breweries.

So why not help support us and join today! How? Just fill in the application form or join online at www.camra.org.uk. Basic membership costs just £16 a year and for this you receive:

- **What's Brewing**, Our lively monthly publication giving hard news from the world of pubs and beer as well as providing information about festivals and special events.
- **Free** or **substantially reduced** entry to all CAMRA beer festivals throughout the UK, including the Great British Beer Festival
- **Discounts** on many CAMRA publications, including our best-selling Good Beer Guide.

Birthdays, Christmas, Father's and Valentine's Days. Stuck for a gift? Not any more!

JOIN BY DIRECT DEBIT AND GET 3 MONTHS FREE

By completing the direct debit form at the bottom of the application form you also get the following benefits: -

- **3 months FREE.** You will get fifteen months membership for the price of twelve in your first year.
- **No reminders.** Renewal will be automatic, you will not need to be reminded as your new membership cards will arrive in the post before the old ones expire.

This Guarantee should be retained for your reference.

The Direct Debit Guarantee

- This Guarantee is offered by all Banks and Building Societies that take part in the Direct Debit Scheme. The efficiency and security of the Scheme is monitored and protected by your own Bank or Building Society.
- If the amounts to be paid or the payment dates change CAMRA will notify you ten working days in advance of your account being debited or as otherwise agreed.
- If an error is made by CAMRA or your Bank or Building Society, you are guaranteed a full and immediate refund from your branch of the amount paid.
- You can cancel a Direct Debit at any time by writing to your Bank or Building Society. Please also send a copy of your letter to us at Campaign for Real Ale Ltd, 230 Hatfield Road, St. Albans, Herts. AL1 4LW

| Title | Surname |
| | |

Membership Application

Please indicate below (circle the amount and payment method) which categories applies:

| Forename(s) | D.O.B |
| | |

Partner Title / Surname (If applicable)

| | |

| Forename(s) | D.O.B |
| | |

Single..............£16
Joint...............£19
Under 26............£9
Under 26 Joint...£12
Retired.............£9
Retired Joint.....£12

Address

- I enclose a cheque, payable to **CAMRA**, for £_____
- I wish to pay by Direct Debit

Postcode

Signed.................................

Tel No.

Date.....................

E-mail

If this a gift, to start on which month?...........................

(origin - V&V 3 – S&SM Branch)

PLEASE POST TO:- CAMRA, 230 Hatfield Road, St. Albans, Herts. AL1 4LW

Instruction to your Bank or Building Society to pay by Direct Debit

To the manager		**Instruction to your Bank or Building Society**
	Bank or Building Society	Please pay CAMRA Direct Debits from the account detailed on this instruction subject to the safeguards assured by the Direct Debit Guarantee. I understand that this instruction may remain with CAMRA and, if so, will be passed electronically to my Bank/Building Society.
Address		
	Postcode	

Name(s) of account holders(s)

| | | | | | | | |

Originator's reference

| 9 | 2 | 6 | 1 | 2 | 9 |

Account Number

Branch Sort Code

Reference number

| Signed | | Date |

93